Homework Helpers

Eureka Math
Grade 3

Special thanks go to the Gordan A. Cain Center and to the Department of Mathematics at Louisiana State University for their support in the development of *Eureka Math*.

Published by the non-profit Great Minds

Copyright © 2015 Great Minds. No part of this work may be reproduced, sold, or commercialized, in whole or in part, without written permission from Great Minds. Non-commercial use is licensed pursuant to a Creative Commons Attribution-NonCommercial-ShareAlike 4.0 license; for more information, go to http://greatminds.net/maps/math/copyright. "Great Minds" and "Eureka Math" are registered trademarks of Great Minds.

Printed in the U.S.A.

This book may be purchased from the publisher at eureka-math.org

10 9 8 7 6 5 4 3 2 1

ISBN 978-1-63255-826-8

Grade 3
Module 1

G3-M1-Lesson 1

1. Solve each number sentence.

> I know this picture shows equal groups because each group has the same number of triangles. There are 3 equal groups of 4 triangles.

3 groups of 4 = **12**

3 fours = **12**

$4 + 4 + 4 = 12$
$3 \times 4 = 12$

> I can multiply to find the total number of triangles because multiplication is the same as repeated addition! 3 groups of 4 is the same as 3×4. There are 12 total triangles, so $3 \times 4 = 12$.

2. Circle the picture that shows 3×2.

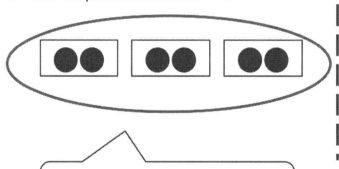

> This picture shows 3×2 because it has 3 groups of 2. The groups are equal.

> This picture does *not* show 3×2 because the groups are not equal. Two of the groups contain 2 objects, but the other only has 1 object.

©2015 Great Minds. eureka-math.org
G3-M1-HWH-1.1.0-07.2015

G3-M1-Lesson 2

1. Use the array below to answer the questions.

> The hearts are arranged in an array, and I know that a row in an array goes straight across. There are 5 rows in this array. Each row has 4 hearts.

a. What is the number of rows? _____5_____

b. What is the number of objects in each row? _____4_____

c. Write a multiplication expression to describe the array. _____5 × 4_____

> I know a multiplication expression is different from an equation because it doesn't have an equal sign.

> I can write the expression 5 × 4 because there are 5 rows with 4 hearts in each row.

2. The triangles below show 2 groups of four.

a. Redraw the triangles as an array that shows 2 rows of four.

> I can redraw the equal groups as an array. I can draw 2 rows with 4 triangles in each row.

b. Compare the groups of triangles to your array. How are they the same? How are they different?

> I need to make sure to explain how they are the same *and* how they are different!

They are the same because they both have the same number of triangles, 8. They are different because the triangles in the array are in rows, but the other triangles are not in rows.

3. Kimberly arranges her 14 markers as an array. Draw an array that Kimberly might make. Then, write a multiplication equation to describe your array.

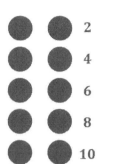

2
4
6
8
10
12
14

$7 \times 2 = 14$

> I can write the equation by writing the number of rows (groups), 7, times the number in each group, 2. The product (total) is 14.

> This problem doesn't tell me the number of rows or the number of objects in each row. I need to use the total, 14, to make an array. Since 14 is an even number, I am going to make rows of 2. I can skip count by 2 and stop when I get to 14.

> I think there are other arrays that would work for a total of 14. I can't wait to see what my friends came up with!

G3-M1-Lesson 3

1. There are ___3___ apples in each basket. How many apples are there in 6 baskets?

a.   Number of groups: ___6___   Size of each group: ___3___

b.   6 × ___3___ = ___18___

c.   There are ___18___ apples altogether.

> Each circle represents 1 basket of apples. There are 6 circles with 3 apples in each circle. The number of groups is 6, and the size of each group is 3. There are 18 apples altogether. I can show this with the equation $6 \times 3 = 18$.

2. There are 3 bananas in each row. How many bananas are there in ___4___ rows?

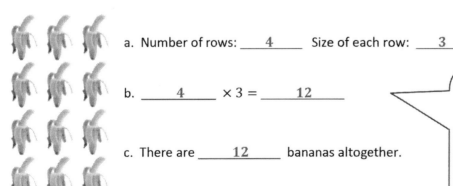

a. Number of rows: ___4___   Size of each row: ___3___

b.   ___4___ × 3 = ___12___

c. There are ___12___ bananas altogether.

> I can show this with the equation $4 \times 3 = 12$. The 4 in the equation is the number of rows, and 3 is the size of each row.

EUREKA
MATH™

The factors tell me the number of groups and the size of each group. I can draw an array with 3 rows and 5 in each row.

3. Draw an array using factors 3 and 5. Then, show a number bond where each part represents the amount in one row.

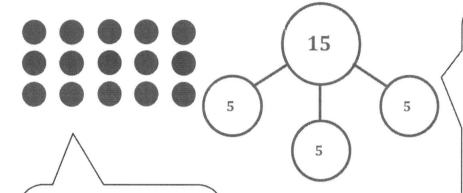

A number bond shows a part–whole relationship. I can draw a number bond with a total of 15 because there are 15 dots in my array.
I can draw 3 parts for my number bond because there are 3 rows in my array.
I can label each part in my number bond as 5 because the size of each row is 5.

My array shows 3 rows of 5. I could have used the same factors, 3 and 5, to draw an array with 5 rows of 3. Then my number bond would have 5 parts, and each part would have a value of 3.

G3-M1-Lesson 4

1. Fill in the blanks.

> The chickens are arranged in an array. I know there are 12 chickens divided equally into 3 groups since each row represents 1 equal group. Each group (row) has 4 chickens. So, the answer in my division sentence, 4, represents the size of the group.

   _____12_____ chickens are divided into _____3_____ equal groups.

   There are _____4_____ chickens in each group.

   $12 \div 3 =$ _____4_____

2. Grace has 16 markers. The picture shows how she placed them on her table. Write a division sentence to represent how she equally grouped her markers.

There are _____4_____ markers in each row.

_____16_____ ÷ _____4_____ = _____4_____

> I can write the total number of markers Grace has, 16, since a division equation begins with the total.

> The 4 represents the number of equal groups. I know there are 4 equal groups because the array shows 4 rows of markers.

> This 4 represents the size of the group. I know this because the array shows 4 markers in each row.

Lesson 4:   Understand the meaning of the unknown as the size of the group in division.

EUREKA MATH

G3-M1-Lesson 5

1. Group the squares to show $8 \div 4 =$ _____ where the unknown represents the number of groups.

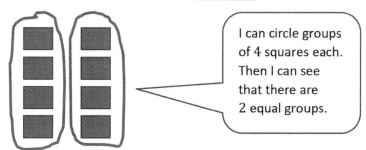

I can circle groups of 4 squares each. Then I can see that there are 2 equal groups.

How many groups are there? _____2_____

$8 \div 4 =$ _____2_____

2. Nathan has 14 apples. He puts 7 apples in each basket. Circle the apples to find the number of baskets Nathan fills.

I can circle groups of 7 apples to find the total number of baskets Nathan fills, 2 baskets.

a. Write a division sentence where the answer represents the number of baskets that Nathan fills.

_____14_____ ÷ _____7_____ = _____2_____

I can write a division sentence beginning with the total number of apples, 14, divided by the number of apples in each basket, 7, to find the number of Nathan's baskets, 2. I can check my answer by comparing it to the circled picture above.

b. Draw a number bond to represent the problem.

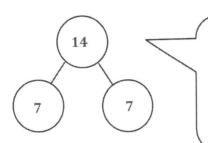

I know that a number bond shows a part–whole relationship. I can label 14 as my whole to represent the total number of Nathan's apples. Then I can draw 2 parts to show the number of baskets Nathan fills and label 7 in each part to show the number of apples in each basket.

3. Lily draws tables. She draws 4 legs on each table for a total of 20 legs.

a. Use a count-by to find the number of tables Lily draws. Make a drawing to match your counting.

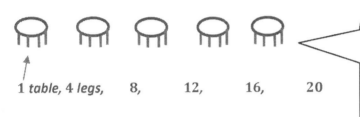

1 table, 4 legs,   8,   12,   16,   20

I can draw models to represent each of Lily's tables. As I draw each table, I can count by four until I reach 20. Then, I can count to find the number of tables Lily draws, 5 tables.

b. Write a division sentence to represent the problem.

_____20_____ ÷ _____4_____ = _____5_____   *Lily draws 5 tables.*

I can write a division sentence beginning with the total number of legs, 20, divided by the number of legs on each table, 4, to find the number of tables Lily draws, 5. I can check my answer by comparing it to my picture and count-by in part (a).

Lesson 5:   Understand the meaning of the unknown as the number of groups in
                                  division.

©2015 Great Minds. eureka-math.org
G3-M1-HWH-1.1.0-07.2015

EUREKA
MATH

G3-M1-Lesson 6

1. Sharon washes 20 bowls. She then dries and stacks the bowls equally into 5 piles. How many bowls are in each pile?

    $20 \div 5 = \underline{\quad 4 \quad}$

    $5 \times \underline{\quad 4 \quad} = 20$

    > I can draw an array with 5 rows to represent Sharon's piles of bowls. I can keep drawing columns of 5 dots until I have a total of 20 dots. The number in each row shows how many bowls are in each pile.

    What is the meaning of the unknown factor and quotient?___*It represents the size of the group.*___

    > I know that the quotient is the answer you get when you divide one number by another number.

    > I can see from my array that both the unknown factor and quotient represent the size of the group.

2. John solves the equation _____ $\times 5 = 35$ by writing and solving $35 \div 5 = $ ___. Explain why John's method works.

    John's method works because in both problems there are 7 groups of 5 and a total of 35. The quotient in a division equation is like finding the unknown factor in a multiplication equation.

    The blanks in John's two equations represent the number of groups. Draw an array to represent the equations.

    > The answer to both of John's equations is 7. I know 7 represents the number of groups, so I can draw 7 rows in my array. Then I can draw 5 dots in each row to show the size of the group for a total of 35 dots in my array.

G3-M1-Lesson 7

1. Draw an array that shows 5 rows of 2.

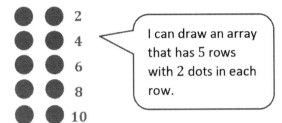

2
4
6
8
10

I can draw an array that has 5 rows with 2 dots in each row.

2. Draw an array that shows 2 rows of 5.

5
10

I can draw an array that has 2 rows with 5 dots in each row.

Write a multiplication sentence where the first factor represents the number of rows.

___5___ × ___2___ = ___10___

I can write a multiplication sentence with 5 as the first factor because 5 is the number of rows. The second factor is 2 because there are 2 dots in each row. I can skip-count by 2 to find the product, 10.

Write a multiplication sentence where the first factor represents the number of rows.

___2___ × ___5___ = ___10___

I can write a multiplication sentence with 2 as the first factor because 2 is the number of rows. The second factor is 5 because there are 5 dots in each row. I can skip-count by 5 to find the product, 10.

3. Why are the factors in your multiplication sentences in a different order?

The factors are in a different order because they mean different things. Problem 1 is 5 rows of 2, and Problem 2 is 2 rows of 5. In Problem 1, the 5 represents the number of rows. In Problem 2, the 5 represents the number of dots in each row.

The arrays show the commutative property. The order of the factors changed because the factors mean different things for each array. The product stayed the same for each array.

Lesson 7:   Demonstrate the commutativity of multiplication, and practice related
facts by skip-counting objects in array models.

EUREKA MATH

4. Write a multiplication sentence to match the number of groups. Skip-count to find the totals.

    a. 7 twos: $\underline{7 \times 2 = 14}$

    b. 2 sevens: $\underline{2 \times 7 = 14}$

> 7 twos is unit form. It means that there are 7 groups of 2. I can represent that with the multiplication equation $7 \times 2 = 14$. 2 sevens means 2 groups of 7, which I can represent with the multiplication equation $2 \times 7 = 14$.

> I see a pattern! 7 twos is equal to 2 sevens. It's the commutative property! The factors switched places and mean different things, but the product didn't change.

5. Find the unknown factor to make each equation true.

    $2 \times 8 = \underline{8} \times \underline{2}$ $\underline{4} \times 2 = 2 \times 4$

> To make true equations, I need to make sure what's on the left of the equal sign is the same as (or equal to) what's on the right of the equal sign.

> I can use the commutative property to help me. I know that $2 \times 8 = 16$ and $8 \times 2 = 16$, so I can write 2 in the first blank. To solve the second problem, I know that $4 \times 2 = 8$ and $2 \times 4 = 8$. I can write 4 in the blank.

©2015 Great Minds. eureka-math.org
G3-M1-HWH-1.1.0-07.2015

G3-M1-Lesson 8

1. Find the unknowns that make the equations true. Then, draw a line to match related facts.

   a. $3 + 3 + 3 + 3 =$ ___12___

   d. $3 \times 6 =$ ___18___

   > $3 + 3 + 3 + 3$ is the same as 4 threes or 4×3, which equals 12. These equations are related because they both show that 4 groups of 3 equal 12.

   b. $3 \times 7 =$ ___21___

   e. ___12___ $= 4 \times 3$

   c. 5 threes + 1 three = ___18___

   f. $21 = 7 \times$ ___3___

   > 5 threes + 1 three = 6 threes. 6 threes is the same as 6 groups of 3 or 6×3, which equals 18. I can use the commutative property to match this equation with $3 \times 6 = 18$.

   > I can use the commutative property to match $3 \times 7 = 21$ and $21 = 7 \times 3$.

2. Fred puts 3 stickers on each page of his sticker album. He puts stickers on 7 pages.

   a. Use circles to draw an array that represents the total number of stickers in Fred's sticker album.

   ● ● ● 3
   ● ● ● 6
   ● ● ● 9
   ● ● ● 12
   ● ● ● 15
   ● ● ● 18
   ● ● ● 21
   ✘ ✘ ✘
   ✘ ✘ ✘
   ✘ ✘ ✘

   > I can draw an array with 7 rows to represent the 7 pages of the sticker album. I can draw 3 circles in each row to represent the 3 stickers that Fred puts on each page.

   > I can draw 3 more rows of 3 to represent the 3 pages and 3 stickers on each page that Fred adds to his sticker album in part (c).

Lesson 8:   Demonstrate the commutativity of multiplication, and practice related facts by skip-counting objects in array models.   **EUREKA MATH**

©2015 Great Minds. eureka-math.org
G3-M1-HWH-1.1.0-07.2015

b. Use your array to write and solve a multiplication sentence to find Fred's total number of stickers.

$$7 \times 3 = 21$$

Fred puts 21 stickers in his sticker album.

> I can write the multiplication equation $7 \times 3 = 21$ to find the total because there are 7 rows in my array with 3 circles in each row. I can use my array to skip-count to find the total, 21.

c. Fred adds 3 more pages to his sticker album. He puts 3 stickers on each new page. Draw x's to show the new stickers on the array in part (a).

d. Write and solve a multiplication sentence to find the new total number of stickers in Fred's sticker album.

$$24, 27, 30$$

$$10 \times 3 = 30$$

Fred has a total of 30 stickers in his sticker album.

> I can continue to skip-count by three from 21 to find the total, 30. I can write the multiplication equation $10 \times 3 = 30$ to find the total because there are 10 rows in my array with 3 in each row. The number of rows changed, but the size of each row stayed the same.

EUREKA MATH

Lesson 8: Demonstrate the commutativity of multiplication, and practice related facts by skip-counting objects in array models.

13

©2015 Great Minds. eureka-math.org
G3-M1-HWH-1.1.0-07.2015

G3-M1-Lesson 9

1. Matt organizes his baseball cards into 3 rows of three. Jenna adds 2 more rows of 3 baseball cards. Complete the equations to describe the total number of baseball cards in the array.

a. $(3 + 3 + 3) + (3 + 3) = $ _____15_____

b. 3 threes + _____2_____ threes = _____5_____ threes

c. _____5_____ $\times 3 = $ _____15_____

> The multiplication equation for this array is $5 \times 3 = 15$ because there are 5 threes or 5 rows of 3, which is a total of 15 baseball cards.

> The total for Matt's baseball cards (the unshaded rectangles) can be represented by $3 + 3 + 3$ because there are 3 rows of 3 baseball cards. The total for Jenna's baseball cards (the shaded rectangles) can be represented by $3 + 3$ because there are 2 rows of 3 baseball cards. This can be represented in unit form with 3 threes +2 threes, which equals 5 threes.

2. $8 \times 3 = $ _____24_____

> I can find the product of 8×3 using the array and the equations below. This problem is different than the problem above because now I am finding two products and subtracting instead of adding.

> The multiplication equation for the whole array is $10 \times 3 = 30$. The multiplication equation for the shaded part is $2 \times 3 = 6$.

$10 \times 3 = $ _30_

$2 \times 3 = $ _6_

$30 - $ _6_ $ = 24$

_8_ $\times 3 = 24$

> To solve 8×3, I can think of 10×3 because that's an easier fact. I can subtract the product of 2×3 from the product of 10×3. $30 - 6 = 24$, so $8 \times 3 = 24$.

EUREKA
MATH

©2015 Great Minds. eureka-math.org
G3-M1-HWH-1.1.0-07.2015

G3-M1-Lesson 10

1. Use the array to help you fill in the blanks.

    $6 \times 2 =$ ___12___

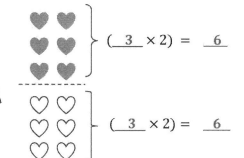

The dotted line in the array shows how I can break apart 6×2 into two smaller facts. Then I can add the products of the smaller facts to find the product of 6×2.

(_3_ × 2) = _6_

(_3_ × 2) = _6_

I know the first factor in each equation is 3 because there are 3 rows in each of the smaller arrays. The product for each array is 6.

$(3 \times 2) + (3 \times 2) =$ _6_ + _6_

_6_ $\times 2 =$ _12_

The expressions in the parentheses represent the smaller arrays. I can add the products of these expressions to find the total number of hearts in the array. The products of the smaller expressions are both 6. $6 + 6 = 12$, so $6 \times 2 = 12$.

Hey, look! It's a doubles fact! $6 + 6 = 12$. I know my doubles facts, so this is easy to solve!

EUREKA
MATH™

Lesson 10: Model the distributive property with arrays to decompose units as a strategy to multiply.

©2015 Great Minds. eureka-math.org
G3-M1-HWH-1.1.0-07.2015

15

2. Lilly puts stickers on a piece of paper. She puts 3 stickers in each row.

   a. Fill in the equations to the right. Use them to draw arrays that show the stickers on the top and bottom parts of Lilly's paper.

I know there are 3 stickers in each row, and this equation also tells me that there are 12 stickers in all on the top of the paper. I can skip-count by 3 to figure out how many rows of stickers there. $3, 6, 9, 12$. I skip-counted 4 threes, so there are 4 rows of 3 stickers. Now I can draw an array with 4 rows of 3.

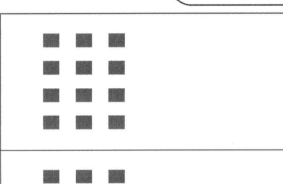

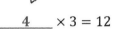 $\underline{\quad 4 \quad} \times 3 = 12$

 $\underline{\quad 2 \quad} \times 3 = 6$

I see 6 rows of 3 altogether. I can use the products of these two smaller arrays to solve 6×3.

I can use the same strategy to find the number of rows in this equation. I skip-counted 2 threes, so there are 2 rows of 3 stickers. Now I can draw an array with 2 rows of 3.

EUREKA
MATH

G3-M1-Lesson 11

1. Mr. Russell organizes 18 clipboards equally into 3 boxes. How many clipboards are in each box? Model the problem with both an array and a labeled tape diagram. Show each column as the number of clipboards in each box.

> I can draw an array with 3 columns because each column represents 1 box of clipboards. I can draw rows of 3 dots until I have a total of 18 dots. I can count how many dots are in each column to solve the problem.

> I know the total number of clipboards is 18, and there are 3 boxes of clipboards. I need to figure out how many clipboards are in each box. I can think of this as division, $18 \div 3 =$ ___, or as multiplication, $3 \times$ ___ $= 18$.

? clipboards

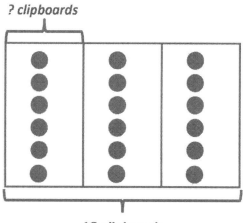

18 clipboards

> I can draw 3 units in my tape diagram to represent the 3 boxes of clipboards. I can label the whole tape diagram with "18 clipboards". I can label one unit in the tape diagram with "? clipboards" because that's what I am solving for. I can draw 1 dot in each unit until I have a total of 18 dots.

There are ___6___ clipboards in each box.

> Look, my array and tape diagram both show units of 6. The columns in my array each have 6 dots, and the units in my tape diagram each have a value of 6.

> I know the answer is 6 because my array has 6 dots in each column. My tape diagram also shows the answer because there are 6 dots in each unit.

2. Caden reads 2 pages in his book each day. How many days will it take him to read a total of 12 pages?

> This problem is different than the other problem because the known information is the total and the size of each group. I need to figure out how many groups there are.

> I can draw an array where each column represents the number of pages Caden reads each day. I can keep drawing columns of 2 until I have a total of 12.

2 *pages*

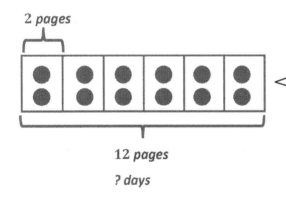

> I can use my array to help me draw a tape diagram. I can draw 6 units of 2 in my tape diagram because my array shows 6 columns of 2.

12 *pages*

? days

$12 \div 2 = 6$

> I know the answer is 6 because my array shows 6 columns of 2, and my tape diagram shows 6 units of 2.

It will take Caden 6 days to read a total of 12 pages.

> I can write a statement to answer the question.

18   Lesson 11:   Model division as the unknown factor in multiplication using arrays and
                            tape diagrams.

©2015 Great Minds. eureka-math.org
G3-M1-HWH-1.1.0-07.2015

G3-M1-Lesson 12

1. Mrs. Harris divides 14 flowers equally into 7 groups for students to study. Draw flowers to find the number in each group. Label known and unknown information on the tape diagram to help you solve.

I know the total number of flowers and the number of groups. I need to solve for the number of flowers in each group.

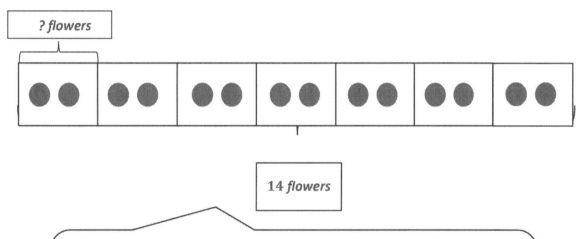

? flowers

14 flowers

I can label the value of the tape diagram as "14 flowers". The number of units in the tape diagram, 7, represents the number of groups. I can label the unknown, which is the value of each unit, as "? flowers". I can draw 1 flower in each unit until I have a total of 14 flowers. I can draw dots instead of flowers to be more efficient!

I can use my tape diagram to solve the problem by counting the number of dots in each unit.

$7 \times \underline{2} = 14$

$14 \div 7 = \underline{2}$

There are ___2___ flowers in each group.

EUREKA
MATH   Lesson 12:   Interpret the quotient as the number of groups or the number of objects   19
                         in each group using units of 2.

©2015 Great Minds. eureka-math.org
G3-M1-HWH-1.1.0-07.2015

2. Lauren finds 2 rocks each day for her rock collection. How many days will it take Lauren to find 16 rocks for her rock collection?

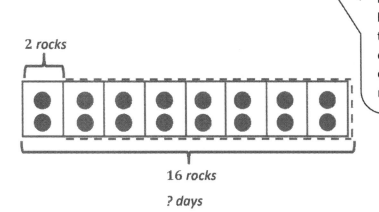

2 rocks

16 rocks

? days

> I know the total is 16 rocks. I know Lauren finds 2 rocks each day, which is the size of each group. I need to figure out how many days it will take her to collect 16 rocks. The unknown is the number of groups.

> I can draw a tape diagram to solve this problem. I can draw a unit of 2 to represent the 2 rocks that Lauren collects each day. I can draw a dotted line to estimate the total days. I can draw units of 2 until I have a total of 16 rocks. I can count the number of units to find the answer.

$16 \div 2 = 8$

> I know the answer is 8 because my tape diagram shows 8 units of 2.

It will take Lauren 8 days to find 16 rocks.

> I can write a statement to answer the question.

20   Lesson 12:   Interpret the quotient as the number of groups or the number of objects
                             in each group using units of 2.

©2015 Great Minds. eureka-math.org
G3-M1-HWH-1.1.0-07.2015

EUREKA
MATH

G3-M1-Lesson 13

1. Mr. Stroup's pet fish are shown below. He keeps 3 fish in each tank.

    a. Circle to show how many fish tanks he has. Then, skip-count to find the total number of fish.

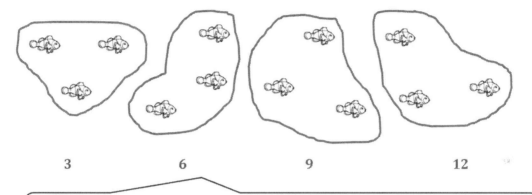

3   6   9   12

> I can circle groups of 3 fish and skip-count by 3 to find the total number of fish. I can count the number of groups to figure out how many fish tanks Mr. Stroup has.

Mr. Stroup has a total of 12 *fish in* 4 *tanks.*

    b. Draw and label a tape diagram to represent the problem.

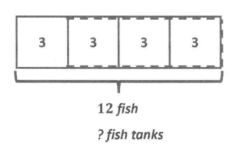

12 fish

? fish tanks

> I can use the picture in part (a) to help me draw a tape diagram. Each fish tank has 3 fish, so I can label each unit with the number 3. I can draw a dotted line to estimate the total fish tanks. I can label the total as 12 fish. Then I can draw units of 3 until I have a total of 12 fish.

> The picture and the tape diagram both show that there are 4 fish tanks. The picture shows 4 equal groups of 3, and the tape diagram shows 4 units of 3.

$\underline{\quad 12 \quad} \div 3 = \underline{\quad 4 \quad}$

Mr. Stroup has __4__ fish tanks.

Lesson 13: Interpret the quotient as the number of groups or the number of objects in each group using units of 3.

©2015 Great Minds. eureka-math.org
G3-M1-HWH-1.1.0-07.2015

21

2. A teacher has 21 pencils. They are divided equally among 3 students. How many pencils does each student get?

? pencils

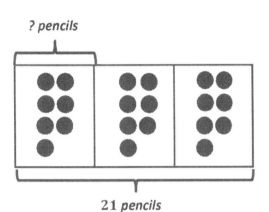

21 pencils

> I can draw a tape diagram to solve this problem. I can draw 3 units to represent the 3 students. I can label the total number of pencils as 21 pencils. I need to figure out how many pencils each student gets.

> I know that I can divide 21 by 3 to solve. I don't know 21 ÷ 3, so I can draw one dot in each unit until I have a total of 21 dots. I can count the number of dots in one unit to find the quotient.

$21 \div 3 = 7$

> I know the answer is 7 because my tape diagram shows 3 units of 7.

Each student will get 7 pencils.

> I can write a statement to answer the question.

Lesson 13:   Interpret the quotient as the number of groups or the number of objects in each group using units of 3.

©2015 Great Minds. eureka-math.org
G3-M1-HWH-1.1.0-07.2015

EUREKA MATH

G3-M1-Lesson 14

1. Mrs. Smith replaces 4 wheels on 3 cars. How many wheels does she replace? Draw and label a tape diagram to solve.

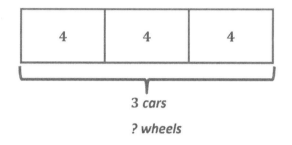

I can draw a tape diagram with 3 units to represent the 3 cars. Each car has 4 wheels, so I can label each unit with the number 4. I need to find the total number of wheels.

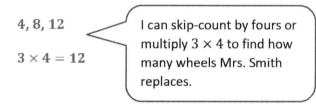

I can skip-count by fours or multiply 3×4 to find how many wheels Mrs. Smith replaces.

Mrs. Smith replaces ___12___ wheels.

2. Thomas makes 4 necklaces. Each necklace has 7 beads. Draw and label a tape diagram to show the total number of beads Thomas uses.

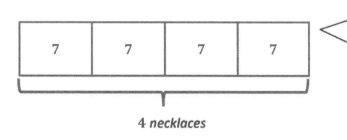

I can draw a tape diagram with 4 units to represent the 4 necklaces. I can label each unit in the tape diagram to show that every necklace has 7 beads. I need to find the total number of beads.

7, 14, 21, 28

4, 8, 12, 16, 20, 24, 28

$4 \times 7 = 28$

I can skip-count 4 sevens, but sevens are still tricky for me. I can skip-count 7 fours instead! I can also multiply 4×7 to find how many beads Thomas uses.

Thomas uses ___28___ beads.

EUREKA MATH   **Lesson 14:**   Skip-count objects in models to build fluency with multiplication facts using units of 4.   **23**

©2015 Great Minds. eureka-math.org
G3-M1-HWH-1.1.0-07.2015

3. Find the total number of sides on 6 squares.

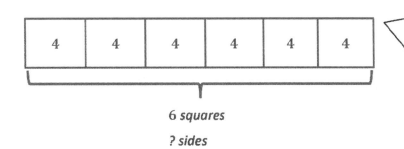

6 *squares*

? *sides*

I can draw a tape diagram with 6 units to represent the 6 squares. All squares have 4 sides, so I can label each unit with the number 4. I need to find the total number of sides.

4, 8, 12, 16, 20, 24

I can skip-count 6 fours or multiply 6 × 4 to find the total number of sides on 6 squares.

$6 \times 4 = 24$

There are 24 sides on 6 squares.

**EUREKA
MATH**

G3-M1-Lesson 15

1. Label the tape diagrams, and complete the equations. Then, draw an array to represent the problems.

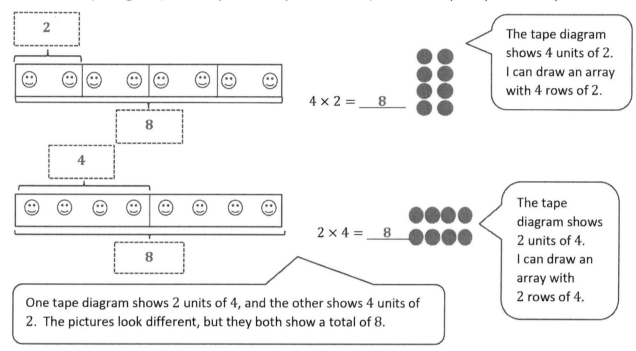

$4 \times 2 = \underline{\ 8\ }$

The tape diagram shows 4 units of 2. I can draw an array with 4 rows of 2.

$2 \times 4 = \underline{\ 8\ }$

The tape diagram shows 2 units of 4. I can draw an array with 2 rows of 4.

One tape diagram shows 2 units of 4, and the other shows 4 units of 2. The pictures look different, but they both show a total of 8.

2. 8 books cost $4 each. Draw and label a tape diagram to show the total cost of the books.

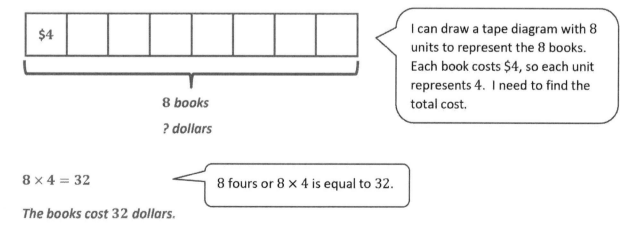

8 books

? dollars

I can draw a tape diagram with 8 units to represent the 8 books. Each book costs $4, so each unit represents 4. I need to find the total cost.

$8 \times 4 = 32$

8 fours or 8×4 is equal to 32.

The books cost 32 dollars.

EUREKA MATH   Lesson 15:   Relate arrays to tape diagrams to model the commutative property of   25
                            multiplication.

©2015 Great Minds. eureka-math.org
G3-M1-HWH-1.1.0-07.2015

3. Liana reads 8 pages from her book each day. How many pages does Liana read in 4 days?

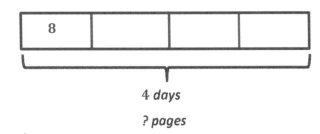

4 *days*

? *pages*

I can draw a tape diagram with 4 units to represent the 4 days. Liana reads 8 pages each day, so each unit represents 8. I need to find the total number of pages.

$4 \times 8 = 32$

Liana reads 32 pages.

I just solved 8×4, and I know that $8 \times 4 = 4 \times 8$. If 8 fours is equal to 32, then 4 eights is also equal to 32.

Lesson 15: Relate arrays to tape diagrams to model the commutative property of multiplication.

©2015 Great Minds. eureka-math.org
G3-M1-HWH-1.1.0-07.2015

G3-M1-Lesson 16

1. Label the array. Then, fill in the blanks below to make true number sentences.

$8 \times 3 = \underline{\ 24\ }$

$(5 \times 3) = \underline{\ 15\ }$

I know that I can break apart 8 threes into 5 threes and 3 threes. I can add the products for 5×3 and 3×3 to find the product for 8×3.

$(3 \times 3) = \underline{\ 9\ }$

$8 \times 3 = (5 \times 3) + (3 \times 3)$
$= \underline{\ 15\ } + \underline{\ 9\ }$
$= \underline{\ 24\ }$

2. The array below shows one strategy for solving 8×4. Explain the strategy using your own words.

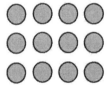

$(5 \times 4) = \underline{\ 20\ }$

8×4 is a tricky fact for me to solve, but 5×4 and 3×4 are both pretty easy facts. I can use them to help me!

$(3 \times 4) = \underline{\ 12\ }$

I split apart the 8 rows of 4 into 5 rows of 4 and 3 rows of 4. I split the array there because my fives facts and my threes facts are easier than my eights facts. I know that $5 \times 4 = 20$ and $3 \times 4 = 12$. I can add those products to find that $8 \times 4 = 32$.

EUREKA MATH

Lesson 16: Use the distributive property as a strategy find related multiplication facts.

27

©2015 Great Minds. eureka-math.org
G3-M1-HWH-1.1.0-07.2015

G3-M1-Lesson 17

1. The baker packs 20 muffins into boxes of 4. Draw and label a tape diagram to find the number of boxes she packs.

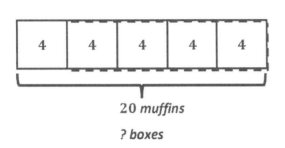

20 *muffins*

? boxes

> I can draw a tape diagram. Each box has 4 muffins, so I can draw a unit and label it 4. I can draw a dotted line to estimate the total number of boxes, because I don't yet know how many boxes there are. I do know the total, so I'll label that as 20 muffins. I'll solve by drawing units of 4 in the dotted part of my tape diagram until I have a total of 20 muffins. Then I can count the number of units to see how many boxes of muffins the baker packs.

$20 \div 4 = \underline{\ \ 5\ \ }$

The baker packs 5 boxes.

2. The waiter arranges 12 plates into 4 equal rows. How many plates are in each row?

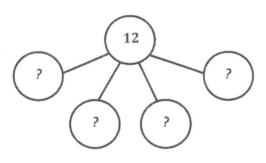

> I can use a number bond to solve. I know that the total number of plates is 12 and that the 12 plates are in 4 rows. Each part in the number bond represents a row of plates.

$12 \div 4 = \underline{\ \ 3\ \ }$

$3 \times 4 = \underline{\ \ 12\ \ }$

> I can divide to solve. I can also think of this as multiplication with an unknown factor.

There are 3 plates in each row.

EUREKA
MATH

3. A teacher has 20 erasers. She divides them equally between 4 students. She finds 12 more erasers and divides these equally between the 4 students as well. How many erasers does each student receive?

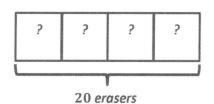

$20 \div 4 = \underline{\ 5\ }$

> I can find the number of erasers each student gets at first when the teacher has 20 erasers.

20 *erasers*

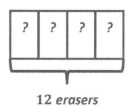

$12 \div 4 = \underline{\ 3\ }$

> I can find how many erasers each student gets when the teacher finds 12 more erasers.

12 *erasers*

5 *erasers* + 3 *erasers* = __8__ *erasers*.

> I can add to find how many total erasers each student gets.

Each student receives 8 erasers.

©2015 Great Minds. eureka-math.org
G3-M1-HWH-1.1.0-07.2015

G3-M1-Lesson 18

1. Match the number bond on an apple with the equation on a bucket that shows the same total.

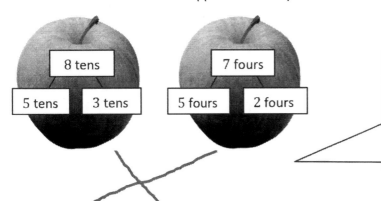

The number bonds in the apples help me see how I can find the total by adding the two smaller parts together. I can match the apples with the equations below that show the same two parts and total.

$(5 \times 4) + (2 \times 4) = 28$

$(5 \times 10) + (3 \times 10) = 80$

2. Solve.

$9 \times 4 = \underline{\quad 36 \quad}$

I can think of this total as 9 fours. There are many ways to break apart 9 fours, but I'm going to break it apart as 5 fours and 4 fours because 5 is a friendly number.

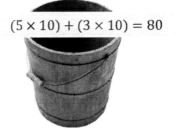

9×4

5×4 4×4

I can use the number bond to help me fill in the blanks. Adding the **products** of these two smaller facts helps me find the product of the larger fact.

$(\underline{\quad 5 \quad} \times 4) + (\underline{\quad 4 \quad} \times 4) = 9 \times 4$

$\underline{\quad 20 \quad} + \underline{\quad 16 \quad} = \underline{\quad 36 \quad}$

$9 \times 4 = \underline{\quad 36 \quad}$

Lesson 18:   Apply the distributive property to decompose units.

©2015 Great Minds. eureka-math.org
G3-M1-HWH-1.1.0-07.2015

3. Mia solves 7×3 using the break apart and distribute strategy. Show an example of what Mia's work might look like below.

5 *threes* + 2 *threes* = 7 *threes*

$(5 \times 3) + (2 \times 3) = 7 \times 3$

$15 + 6 = 21$

I can use the number bond to help me write the equations. Then I can find the products of the two smaller facts and add them to find the product of the larger fact.

The number bond helps me see the break apart and distribute strategy easily. I can think of 7×3 as 7 threes. Then I can break it apart as 5 threes and 2 threes.

G3-M1-Lesson 19

1. Solve.

$28 \div 4 = \underline{\quad 7 \quad}$

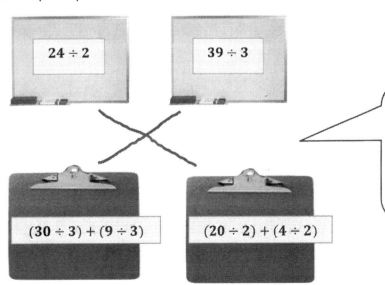

$(20 \div 4) = \underline{\quad 5 \quad}$

$(8 \div 4) = \underline{\quad 2 \quad}$

$(28 \div 4) = (20 \div 4) + (\underline{\quad 8 \quad} \div 4)$

$= \underline{\quad 5 \quad} + \underline{\quad 2 \quad}$

$= \underline{\quad 7 \quad}$

> This shows how we can add the quotients of two smaller facts to find the quotient of the larger one. The array can help me fill in the blanks.

> This array shows a total of 28 triangles. I see that the dotted line breaks apart the array after the fifth row. There are 5 fours above the dotted line and 2 fours below the dotted line.

Match equal expressions.

$24 \div 2$

$39 \div 3$

$(30 \div 3) + (9 \div 3)$

$(20 \div 2) + (4 \div 2)$

> I can match the larger division problem found on the whiteboard to the two smaller division problems added together on the clipboard below.

Lesson 19:   Apply the distributive property to decompose units.

©2015 Great Minds. eureka-math.org
G3-M1-HWH-1.1.0-07.2015

2. Chloe draws the array below to find the answer to $48 \div 4$. Explain Chloe's strategy.

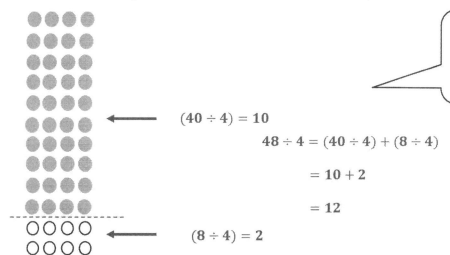

For this problem, I can count the number of rows in this array to check my answer.

$(40 \div 4) = 10$

$$48 \div 4 = (40 \div 4) + (8 \div 4)$$

$$= 10 + 2$$

$$= 12$$

$(8 \div 4) = 2$

Chloe breaks apart 48 as 10 fours and 2 fours. 10 fours equals 40, and 2 fours equals 8. So, she does
$40 \div 4$ and $8 \div 4$ and adds the answers to get $48 \div 4$, which equals 12.

G3-M1-Lesson 20

1. Thirty-five students are eating lunch at 5 tables. Each table has the same number of students.

    a. How many students are sitting at each table?

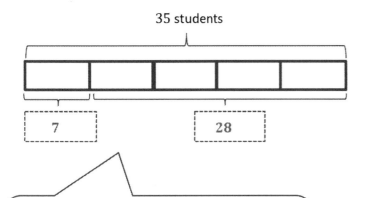

35 students

7

28

> I know there are a total of 35 students eating lunch at 5 tables. I know each table has the same number of students. I need to figure out how many students are sitting at each table. The unknown is the size of each group.

> Each unit in my tape diagram represents 1 table. Since there are 35 students and 5 tables, I can divide 35 by 5 to find that each table has 7 students. This tape diagram shows that there are 5 units of 7 for a total of 35.

$35 \div 5 = 7$

There are 7 students sitting at each table.

    b. How many students are sitting at 4 tables?

$4 \times 7 = 28$
There are 28 students sitting at 4 tables.

> Since I now know there are 7 students sitting at each table, I can multiply the number of tables, 4, by 7 to find that there are 28 students sitting at 4 tables. I can see this in the tape diagram: 4 units of 7 equal 28.

> I can write a number sentence and a statement to answer the question.

Lesson 20:   Solve two-step word problems involving multiplication and division, and assess the reasonableness of answers.

EUREKA MATH™

2. The store has 30 notebooks in packs of 3. Six packs of notebooks are sold. How many packs of notebooks are left?

I can draw a tape diagram that shows 30 notebooks in packs of 3. I can find the total number of packs by dividing 30 by 3 to get 10 total packs of notebooks.

I know the total is 30 notebooks. I know the notebooks are in packs of 3. First I need to figure out how many total packs of notebooks are in the store.

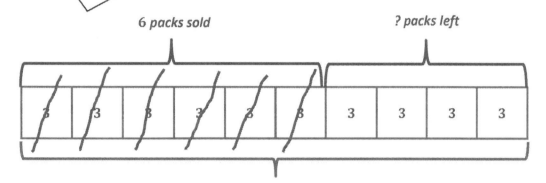

6 packs sold   ? packs left

30 notebooks

? total packs

Now that I know the total number of packs is 10, I can find the number of packs that are left.

$30 \div 3 = 10$

There are a total of 10 packs of notebooks at the store.

$10 - 6 = 4$

There are 4 packs of notebooks left.

I can show the packs that were sold on my tape diagram by crossing off 6 units of 3. Four units of 3 are not crossed off, so there are 4 packs of notebooks left. I can write a subtraction equation to represent the work on my tape diagram.

EUREKA
MATH™   Lesson 20:   Solve two-step word problems involving multiplication and division, and   35
                         assess the reasonableness of answers.

             ©2015 Great Minds. eureka-math.org
             G3-M1-HWH-1.1.0-07.2015

G3-M1-Lesson 21

1. John has a reading goal. He checks out 3 boxes of 7 books from the library. After finishing them, he realizes that he beat his goal by 5 books! Label the tape diagrams to find John's reading goal.

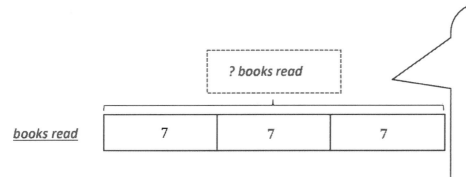

Each unit in this tape diagram represents 1 box of John's library books. The number of books in each box (the size) is 7 books. So I can multiply 3×7 to find the number of books John reads.

$3 \times 7 = 21$

John reads 21 books.

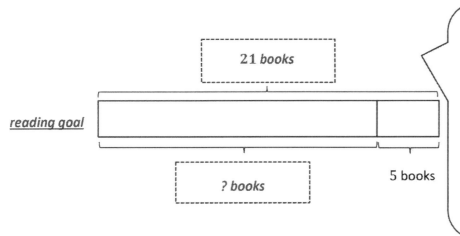

I can draw a tape diagram that shows 21 as the total because John reads 21 books. I can label one part as 5 because John beat his reading goal by 5 books. When I know a total and one part, I know I can subtract to find the

$21 - 5 = 16$

John's goal was to read ___16___ books.

I can check back to see if my statement answers the question.

Lesson 21:   Solve two-step word problems involving all four operations, and assess the reasonableness of answers.

EUREKA MATH

2. Mr. Kim plants 20 trees around the neighborhood pond. He plants equal numbers of maple, pine, spruce, and birch trees. He waters the spruce and birch trees before it gets dark. How many trees does Mr. Kim still need to water? Draw and label a tape diagram.

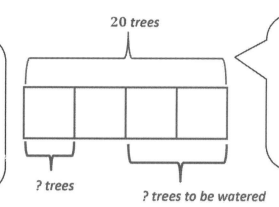

20 trees

I know Mr. Kim plants a total of 20 trees. He plants an equal number of 4 types of trees. This is the number of groups. So, the unknown is the size of each group.

I can draw a tape diagram that has 4 units to represent the 4 types of trees. I can label the whole as 20, and I can divide 20 by 4 to find the value of each unit.

? trees

? trees to be watered

I know that Mr. Kim waters the spruce and birch trees, so he still needs to water the maple and pine trees. I can see from my tape diagram that 2 units of 5 trees still need to be watered. I can multiply 2 × 5 to find that 10 trees still need to be watered.

$20 \div 4 = 5$
Mr. Kim plants 5 of each type of tree.

$2 \times 5 = 10$
Mr. Kim still needs to water 10 trees.

$20 - 10 = 10$
Mr. Kim still needs to water 10 trees.

Or I can subtract the number of trees watered, 10, from the total number of trees to find the answer.

EUREKA MATH™

Lesson 21: Solve two-step word problems involving all four operations, and assess the reasonableness of answers.

37

©2015 Great Minds. eureka-math.org
G3-M1-HWH-1.1.0-07.2015

Homework Helpers

Grade 3
Module 2

G3-M2-Lesson 1

The table to the right shows how much time it takes each of the 5 students to run 100 meters.

Eric	19 seconds
Woo	20 seconds
Sharon	24 seconds
Steven	18 seconds
Joyce	22 seconds

a. Who is the fastest runner?

Steven is the fastest runner.

> I know Steven is the fastest runner because the chart shows me that he ran 100 meters in the least number of seconds, 18 seconds.

b. Who is the slowest runner?

Sharon is the slowest runner.

> I know Sharon is the slowest runner because the chart shows me that she ran 100 meters in the most number of seconds, 24 seconds.

c. How many seconds faster did Eric run than Sharon?

$24 - 19 = 5$

Eric ran 5 seconds faster than Sharon.

> I can subtract Eric's time from Sharon's time to find how much faster Eric ran than Sharon. I can use the compensation strategy to think of subtracting $24 - 19$ as $25 - 20$ to get 5. It is much easier for me to subtract $25 - 20$ than $24 - 19$.

G3-M2-Lesson 2

Follow the directions to label the number line below.

a. Susan practices piano between 3:00 p.m. and 4:00 p.m. Label the first and last tick marks as 3:00 p.m. and 4:00 p.m.

3:00 *p.m.*   4:00 *p.m.*

I can label this first tick mark as 3:00 p.m. and the last tick mark as 4:00 p.m. to show the hour interval Susan practices piano.

b. Each interval represents 5 minutes. Count by fives starting at 0, or 3:00 p.m. Label each 5-minute interval below the number line up to 4:00 p.m.

3:00 *p.m.*   4:00 *p.m.*

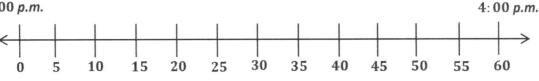

0   5   10   15   20   25   30   35   40   45   50   55   60

I know there are 60 minutes between 3:00 p.m. and 4:00 p.m. I can label 0 minutes below where I wrote 3:00 p.m. and label 60 minutes below where I wrote 4:00 p.m.

I can skip-count by fives to label each 5-minute interval from left to right, starting with 0 and ending with 60.

EUREKA
MATH

c. Susan warms up her fingers by playing the scales until 3:10 p.m. Plot a point on the number line to represent this time. Above the point, write *W*.

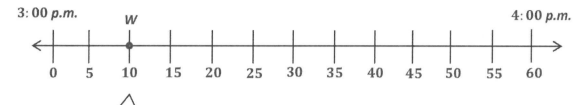

I can find 3:10 p.m. by putting my finger on 3:00 p.m. and moving it to the right as I skip-count intervals until I reach 3:10 p.m. Then I can draw a dot to plot the location of this point on the number line. I can label this point W to represent Susan's warm-up time.

EUREKA
MATH

Lesson 2:   Relate skip-counting by fives on the clock and telling time to a
            continuous measurement model, the number line.

3

©2015 Great Minds. eureka-math.org
G3-M2-HWH-1.3.0-09.2015

G3-M2-Lesson 3

The clock shows what time Caleb starts playing outside on Monday afternoon.

a. What time does he start playing outside?

Start

Caleb starts playing outside at 2: 32 *p.m.*

> I can find the minutes on this analog clock by counting by fives and ones, beginning on the 12, as zero minutes.

b. He plays outside for 19 minutes. What time does he finish playing?

Caleb finishes playing outside at 2: 51 *p.m.*

> I can use different strategies to find the time Caleb finishes playing. The most efficient strategy is to add 20 minutes to 2: 32 to get 2: 52, and then subtract 1 minute to get 2: 51.

c. Draw hands on the clock to the right to show what time Caleb finishes playing.

Finish

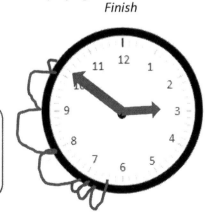

> I can check my answer from part (b) by counting by fives and ones on the clock, and then draw the hands on the clock. My minute hand is exactly at 51 minutes, but my hour hand is close to the 3 since it is almost 3: 00.

Lesson 3:   Count by fives and ones on the number line as a strategy to tell time to
                           the nearest minute on the clock.

                  ©2015 Great Minds. eureka-math.org
                  G3-M2-HWH-1.3.0-09.2015

**EUREKA
MATH**

d. Label the first and last tick marks with 2:00 p.m. and 3:00 p.m. Then, plot Caleb's start and finish times. Label his start time with a *B* and his finish time with an *F*.

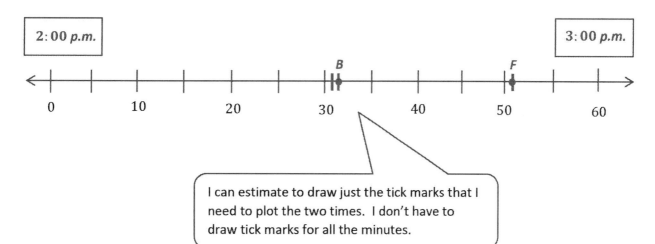

I can estimate to draw just the tick marks that I need to plot the two times. I don't have to draw tick marks for all the minutes.

EUREKA
MATH™

Lesson 3:   Count by fives and ones on the number line as a strategy to tell time to
            the nearest minute on the clock.

©2015 Great Minds. eureka-math.org
G3-M2-HWH-1.3.0-09.2015

5

G3-M2-Lesson 4

Use a number line to answer the problems below.

1. Celina cleans her room for 42 minutes. She starts at 9:04 a.m. What time does Celina finish cleaning her room?

> I can draw a number line to help me figure out when Celina finishes cleaning her room. On the number line, I can label the first tick mark 0 and the last tick mark 60. Then I can label the hours and the 5-minute intervals.

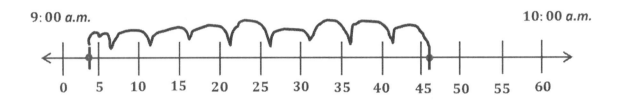

9:00 a.m.   10:00 a.m.

0   5   10   15   20   25   30   35   40   45   50   55   60

Celina finishes cleaning her room at 9:46 a.m.

> I can plot 9:04 a.m. on the number line. Then I can count 2 minutes to 9:06 and 40 minutes by fives until 9:46. 42 minutes after 9:04 a.m. is 9:46 a.m.

2. The school orchestra puts on a concert for the school. The concert lasts 35 minutes. It ends at 1:58 p.m. What time did the concert start?

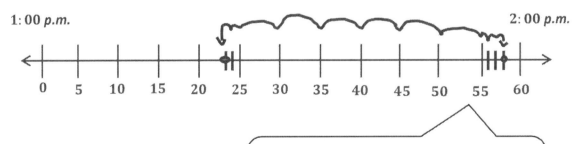

1:00 p.m.   2:00 p.m.

0   5   10   15   20   25   30   35   40   45   50   55   60

The concert started at 1:23 p.m.

> I can plot 1:58 p.m. on the number line. Then I can count backwards from 1:58 by ones to 1:55, by fives to 1:25, and by ones to 1:23. 1:23 p.m. is 35 minutes before 1:58 p.m.

Lesson 4:   Solve word problems involving time intervals within 1 hour by counting
                         backward and forward using the number line and clock.

EUREKA MATH

G3-M2-Lesson 5

Luke exercises. He stretches for 8 minutes, runs for 17 minutes, and walks for 10 minutes.

a. How many total minutes does he spend exercising?

> I can draw a tape diagram to show all the known information. I see all the parts are given, but the whole is unknown. So, I can label the whole with a question mark.

? minutes

8 min	17 min	10 min

> I can estimate to draw the parts of my tape diagram to match the lengths of the minutes. 8 minutes is the shortest time, so I can draw it as the shortest unit. 17 minutes is the longest time, so I can draw it as the longest unit.

$$8 + 17 + 10 = 35$$

Luke spends a total of 35 minutes exercising.

> I can write an addition equation to find the total number of minutes Luke spends exercising. I also need to remember to write a statement that answers the question.

EUREKA MATH   **Lesson 5:**   Solve word problems involving time intervals within 1 hour by adding and subtracting on the number line.   7

©2015 Great Minds. eureka-math.org
G3-M2-HWH-1.3.0-09.2015

b. Luke wants to watch a movie that starts at $1:55$ p.m. It takes him 10 minutes to take a shower and 15 minutes to drive to the theater. If Luke starts exercising at $1:00$ p.m., can he make it on time for the movie? Explain your reasoning.

> I can draw a number line to show my reasoning. I can plot the starting time as $1:35$ because I know it takes Luke 35 minutes to exercise from part (a). Then I can add 10 minutes for his shower and an additional 15 minutes for the drive to the theater.

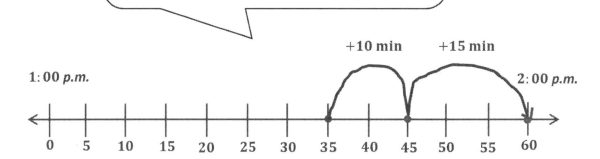

$1:00$ p.m. $2:00$ p.m.

No, Luke can't make it on time for the movie. From the number line, I can see that he will be five minutes late.

> I can see on the number line that Luke will be at the theater at $2:00$ p.m. The movie starts at $1:55$ p.m., so he'll be 5 minutes too late.

EUREKA
MATH™

G3-M2-Lesson 6

1. Use the chart to help you answer the following questions:

1 kilogram	100 grams	10 grams	1 gram

a. Bethany puts a marker that weighs 10 grams on a pan balance. How many 1-gram weights does she need to balance the scale?

Bethany needs ten 1-gram weights to balance the scale.

I know that it takes ten 1-gram weights to equal 10 grams.

b. Next, Bethany puts a 100-gram bag of beans on a pan balance. How many 10-gram weights does she need to balance the scale?

Bethany needs ten 10-gram weights to balance the scale.

I know that it takes ten 10-gram weights to equal 100 grams.

c. Bethany then puts a book that weighs 1 kilogram on a pan balance. How many 100-gram weights does she need to balance the scale?

Bethany needs ten 100-gram weights to balance the scale.

I know that it takes ten 100-gram weights to equal 1 kilogram, or 1,000 grams.

d. What pattern do you notice in parts (a)–(c)?

I notice that to make a weight in the chart it takes ten of the lighter weight to the right in the chart. For example, to make 100 grams, it takes ten 10-gram weights, and to make 1 kilogram, or 1,000 grams, it takes ten 100-gram weights. It's just like the place value chart!

EUREKA MATH™   Lesson 6:   Build and decompose a kilogram to reason about the size and weight of 1 kilogram, 100 grams, 10   9
grams, and 1 gram.

©2015 Great Minds. eureka-math.org
G3-M2-HWH-1.3.0-09.2015

2. Read each digital scale. Write each weight using the word *kilogram* or *gram* for each measurement.

_____153 *grams*_____   _____3 *kilograms*_____

I can write 153 grams because I know that the letter g is used to abbreviate grams.

I can write 3 kilograms because I know that the letters kg are used to abbreviate kilograms.

10   Lesson 6:   Build and decompose a kilogram to reason about the size and weight of 1 kilogram, 100 grams, 10 grams, and 1 gram.

©2015 Great Minds. eureka-math.org
G3-M2-HWH-1.3.0-09.2015

EUREKA
MATH

G3-M2-Lesson 7

1. Match each object with its approximate weight.

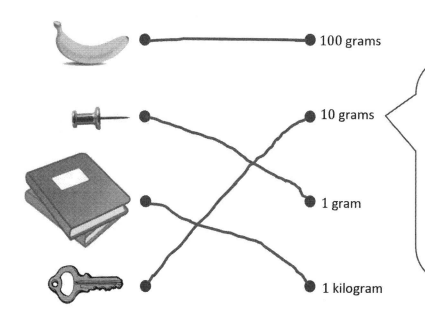

100 grams

10 grams

1 gram

1 kilogram

> I know that the tack is the lightest object, so it must weigh about 1 gram. I also know that the books are the heaviest, so they must weigh about 1 kilogram. I know that the key is lighter than the banana, so the key must weigh about 10 grams and the banana must weigh about 100 grams.

2. Jessica weighs her dog on a digital scale. She writes 8, but she forgets to record the unit. Which unit of measurement is correct, grams or kilograms? How do you know?

The weight of Jessica's dog needs to be recorded as 8 kilograms. Kilograms is the correct unit because 8 grams is about the same weight as 8 paperclips. It wouldn't make sense for her dog to weigh about the same as 8 paperclips.

3. Read and write the weight below. Write the word *kilogram* or *gram* with the measurement.

> I know the unit is grams because there is a letter g on the scale. I can use the image to the right of the scale to determine that each tick mark between 140 grams and 150 grams represents 1 gram. The fruit weighs 146 grams.

146 grams

EUREKA MATH

Lesson 7: Develop estimation strategies by reasoning about the weight in kilograms of a series of familiar objects to establish mental benchmark measures.

11

©2015 Great Minds. eureka-math.org
G3-M2-HWH-1.3.0-09.2015

G3-M2-Lesson 8

The weights below show the weight of the apples in each bucket.

Bucket A   Bucket B   Bucket C
9 kg   7 kg   14 kg

> Bucket C weighs 14 kg, and Bucket B weighs 7 kg. I know that $14 - 7 = 7$, so Bucket C weighs 7 kg more.

a. The apples in Bucket___C___are the heaviest.

b. The apples in Bucket___B___are the lightest.

c. The apples in Bucket C are___7___kilograms heavier than the apples in Bucket B.

d. What is the total weight of the apples in all three buckets?

9 kg	7 kg	14 kg

? kilograms of apples

$$9 + 7 + 14 = 30$$

The total weight of the apples is 30 kilograms.

> I can use a tape diagram to show the weight of each bucket of apples. Then, I can add each apple's weight to find the total weight of the apples.

e. Rebecca and her 2 sisters equally share all of the apples in Bucket A. How many kilograms of apples do they each get?

? kg	? kg	? kg

9 kilograms of apples

$$9 \div 3 = 3$$

Each sister gets 3 kilograms of apples.

> I know that I'm dividing 9 kilograms into 3 equal groups because 3 people are sharing the apples in Bucket A. When I know the total and the number of equal groups, I divide to find the size of each group!

    Lesson 8:   Solve one-step word problems involving metric weights within 100 and estimate to r̶e̶ **EUREKA** solutions.   **MATH**™

f. Mason gives 3 kilograms of apples from Bucket B to his friend. He uses 2 kilograms of apples from Bucket B to make apple pies. How many kilograms of apples are left in Bucket B?

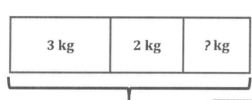

$7 - 5 = 2$

There are 2 kilograms of apples left in Bucket B.

I know that 3 kg of apples were given away and 2 kg of apples were used for apple pies. That means that 5 kg of apples were taken out of Bucket B. It had 7 kg in it to start with, and $7 - 5 = 2$. There are 2 kg of apples left.

g. Angela picks another bucket of apples, Bucket D. The apples in Bucket C are 6 kilograms heavier than the apples in Bucket D. How many kilograms of apples are in Bucket D?

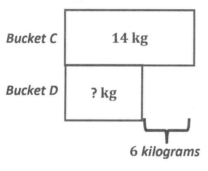

I can draw a double tape diagram to model the problem. I know that the apples in Bucket D weigh 6 kg less than the apples in Bucket C.

I can subtract to find the weight of the apples in Bucket D.

$14 - 6 = 8$

There are 8 kilograms of apples in Bucket D.

h. What is the total weight of the apples in Buckets C and D?

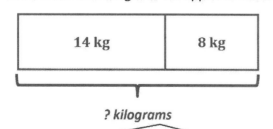

$14 + 8 = 22$

The total weight of the apples in Buckets C and D is 22 kilograms.

To find the total weight of the apples in Buckets C and D, I need to add. I know that $14 + 8 = 22$, so the total weight of the apples in Buckets C and D is 22 kilograms.

EUREKA MATH   Lesson 8:   Solve one-step word problems involving metric weights within 100 and estimate to reason about   13
solutions.

©2015 Great Minds. eureka-math.org
G3-M2-HWH-1.3.0-09.2015

G3-M2-Lesson 9

1. Ben makes 4 batches of cookies for the bake sale. He uses 5 milliliters of vanilla for each batch. How many milliliters of vanilla does he use in all?

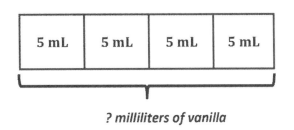

? milliliters of vanilla

I can draw a tape diagram that has 4 units to represent the 4 batches of cookies. I can label each unit as 5 mL to represent the amount of vanilla used in each batch.

$4 \times 5 = 20$

I can multiply 4×5 to find the total amount of vanilla.

Ben uses 20 milliliters of vanilla.

2. Mrs. Gillette pours 3 glasses of juice for her children. Each glass holds 321 milliliters of juice. How much juice does Mrs. Gillette pour in all?

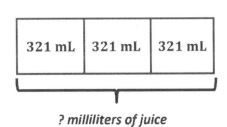

? milliliters of juice

I can draw a tape diagram to model the problem. I can draw 3 units of 321 mL. I need to solve for the total amount of juice.

$321 + 321 + 321 = 963$

Mrs. Gillette pours 963 milliliters of juice.

I could solve using the expression, 3×321, but I don't know how to do that kind of multiplication yet. I can solve with repeated addition.

©2015 Great Minds. eureka-math.org
G3-M2-HWH-1.3.0-09.2015

3. Gabby uses a 4-liter bucket to give her pony water. How many buckets of water will Gabby need in order to give her pony 28 liters of water?

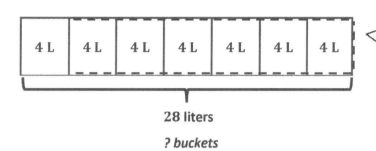

I can draw a tape diagram. I know the total is 28 liters and the size of each unit is 4 liters. I need to solve for the number of units (buckets).

28 liters

? buckets

$28 \div 4 = 7$

Gabby needs 7 buckets of water.

Since I know the total and the size of each unit, I can divide to solve.

4. Elijah makes 12 liters of punch for his birthday party. He pours the punch equally into 4 bowls. How many liters of punch are in each bowl?

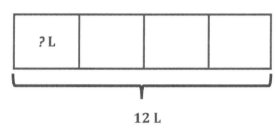

I can draw a tape diagram. I know the total is 12 liters and there are 4 bowls or units. I need to solve for the number of liters in each bowl.

12 L

$12 \div 4 = 3$

Since I know the total and the number of units, I can divide to solve.

Elijah pours 3 liters of punch into each bowl.

I can divide to solve Problems 3 and 4, but the unknowns in each problem are different. In Problem 3, I solved for the number of groups/units. In Problem 4, I solved for the size of each group/unit.

EUREKA MATH™   Lesson 9:   Decompose a liter to reason about the size of 1 liter, 100 milliliters, 10 milliliters, and 1 milliliter.   15

©2015 Great Minds. eureka-math.org
G3-M2-HWH-1.3.0-09.2015

G3-M2-Lesson 10

1. Estimate the amount of liquid in each container to the nearest liter.

The liquid in this container is between 3 liters and 4 liters. Since it is more than halfway to the next liter, 4 liters, I can estimate that there are about 4 liters of liquid.

__4 liters__

The liquid in this container is at exactly 5 liters.

__5 liters__

The liquid in this container is between 3 liters and 4 liters. Since it is less than halfway to the next liter, 4 liters, I can estimate that there are about 3 liters of liquid.

__3 liters__

Lesson 10:   Estimate and measure liquid volume in liters and milliliters using the vertical number   **EUREKA MATH**

2. Manny is comparing the capacity of buckets that he uses to water his vegetable garden. Use the chart to answer the questions.

Bucket	Capacity in Liters
Bucket 1	17
Bucket 2	12
Bucket 3	23

a. Label the number line to show the capacity of each bucket. Bucket 2 has been done for you.

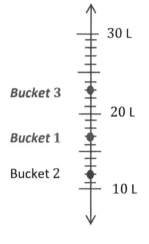

I can use the tick marks to help me locate the correct place on the number line for each bucket. I can label Bucket 1 at 17 liters and Bucket 3 at 23 liters.

b. Which bucket has the greatest capacity?

Bucket 3 *has the greatest capacity.*

c. Which bucket has the smallest capacity?

Bucket 2 *has the smallest capacity.*

I can use the vertical number line to help me answer both of these questions. I can see that the point I plotted for Bucket 3 is higher up the number line than the others, so it has a larger capacity than the others. I also see that the point I plotted for Bucket 2 is lowest on the number line, so it has the smallest capacity.

d. Which bucket has a capacity of about 10 liters?

Bucket 2 *has a capacity of about* 10 *liters.*

I notice that Bucket 2 is closest to 10 liters, so it has a capacity of about 10 liters.

e. Use the number line to find how many more liters Bucket 3 holds than Bucket 2.

Bucket 3 *holds* 11 *more liters than Bucket* 2.

To solve this problem, I can count up on the number line from Bucket 2 to Bucket 3. I'll start at 12 liters because that is the capacity of Bucket 2. I count up 8 tick marks to 20 liters, and then I count 3 more tick marks to 23, which is the capacity of Bucket 3. I know that $8 + 3 = 11$, so Bucket 3 holds 11 more liters than Bucket 2.

G3-M2-Lesson 11

1. Together the weight of a banana and an apple is 291 grams. The banana weighs 136 grams. How much does the apple weigh?

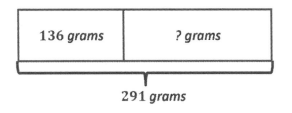

> I can draw a tape diagram to model the problem. The total is 291 grams, and one part—the weight of the banana—is 136 grams. I can subtract to find the other part, the weight of the apple.

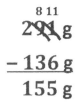

> I can use the standard algorithm to subtract. I can unbundle 1 ten to make 10 ones. Now there are 2 hundreds, 8 tens, and 11 ones.

The apple weighs 155 *grams.*

2. Sandy uses a total of 21 liters of water to water her flowerbeds. She uses 3 liters of water for each flowerbed. How many flowerbeds does Sandy water?

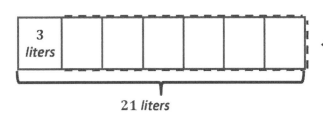

> I can draw a tape diagram to model the problem. The total is 21 liters, and each unit represents the amount of water Sandy uses for each flowerbed, 3 liters. I can see that the unknown is the number of units (groups).

$21 \div 3 = 7$

> I can divide to find the total number of units, which represents the number of flowerbeds.

Sandy waters 7 *flowerbeds.*

> Now that I know the answer, I can draw the rest of the units in my tape diagram, to show a total of 7 units.

©2015 Great Minds. eureka-math.org
G3-M2-HWH-1.3.0-09.2015

G3-M2-Lesson 12

1. Complete the chart.

> I measured the width of a picture frame. It was 24 centimeters wide.

Object	Measurement (in cm)	The object measures between (which two tens)...	Length rounded to the nearest 10 cm
Width of picture frame	24 cm	__20__ and __30__ cm	20 cm

> I can use a vertical number line to help me round 24 cm to the nearest 10 cm.

> The endpoints on my vertical number line help me know which two tens the width of the picture frame is in between.

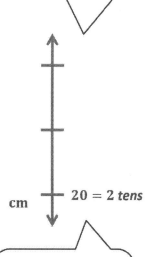

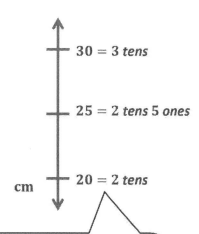

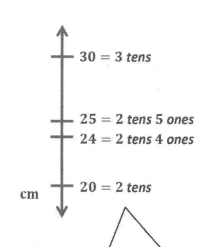

> There are 2 tens in 24, so I can label this endpoint as 2 tens or 20.

> One more ten than 2 tens is 3 tens, so I can label the other endpoint as 3 tens or 30. Halfway between 2 tens and 3 tens is 2 tens 5 ones. I can label the halfway point as 2 tens 5 ones or 25.

> I can plot 24 or 2 tens 4 ones on the vertical number line. I can easily see that 24 is less than halfway between 2 tens and 3 tens. That means that 24 cm rounded to the nearest 10 cm is 20 cm.

2. Measure the liquid in the beaker to the nearest 10 milliliters.

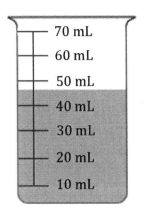

I can use the beaker to help me round the amount of liquid to the nearest 10 mL. I can see that the liquid is between 40 (4 tens) and 50 (5 tens). I can also see that the liquid is more than halfway between 4 tens and 5 tens. That means that the amount of liquid rounds up to the next ten milliliters, 50 mL.

There are about___50___ milliliters of liquid in the beaker.

The word *about* tells me that this is not the exact amount of liquid in the beaker.

G3-M2-Lesson 13

1. Round to the nearest ten. Draw a number line to model your thinking.

a. $52 \approx$ __50__

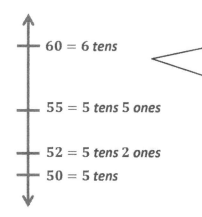

I can draw a vertical number line with endpoints of 50 and 60 and a halfway point of 55. When I plot 52 on the vertical number line, I can see that it is less than halfway between 50 and 60. So 52 rounded to the nearest ten is 50.

b. $152 \approx$ __150__

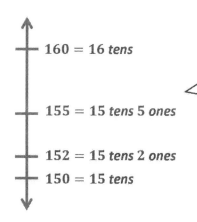

I can draw a vertical number line with endpoints of 150 and 160 and a halfway point of 155. When I plot 152 on the vertical number line, I can see that it is less than halfway between 150 and 160. So 152 rounded to the nearest ten is 150.

Look, my vertical number lines for parts (a) and (b) are almost the same! The only difference is that all the numbers in part (b) are 100 more than the numbers in part (a).

2. Amelia pours 63 mL of water into a beaker. Madison pours 56 mL of water into Amelia's beaker. Round the total amount of water in the beaker to the nearest 10 milliliters. Model your thinking using a number line.

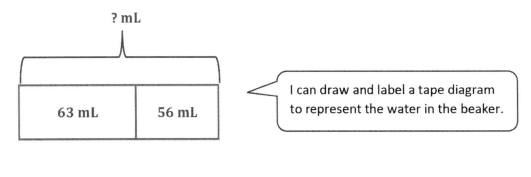

? mL

63 mL   56 mL

> I can draw and label a tape diagram to represent the water in the beaker.

63 mL + 56 mL = 119 mL

> I can find the total amount of water in the beaker by adding 63 mL and 56 mL.

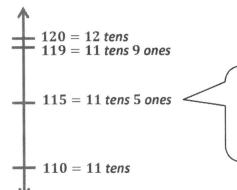

120 = 12 *tens*
119 = 11 *tens* 9 *ones*

115 = 11 *tens* 5 *ones*

110 = 11 *tens*

> I can use a vertical number line to round 119 mL to the nearest 10 milliliters. I can see that 119 mL is more than halfway between 110 mL and 120 mL. So 119 mL rounded to the nearest 10 mL is 120 mL.

There are about 120 mL *of water in the beaker.*

G3-M2-Lesson 14

1. Round to the nearest hundred. Draw a number line to model your thinking.

a. $234 \approx$ __200__

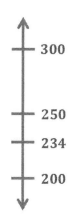

I can draw a vertical number line with endpoints of 200 and 300 and a halfway point of 250. When I plot 234 on the vertical number line, I can see that it is less than halfway between 200 and 300. So 234 rounded to the nearest hundred is 200.

b. $1,234 \approx$ __1,200__

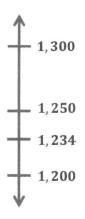

I can draw a vertical number line with endpoints of 1,200 and 1,300 and a halfway point of 1,250. When I plot 1,234 on the vertical number line, I can see that it is less than halfway between 1,200 and 1,300. So 1,234 rounded to the nearest hundred is 1,200.

Look, my vertical number lines for parts (a) and (b) are almost the same! The only difference is that all the numbers in part (b) are 1,000 more than the numbers in part (a).

©2015 Great Minds. eureka-math.org
G3-M2-HWH-1.3.0-09.2015

2. There are 1,365 students at Park Street School. Kate and Sam round the number of students to the nearest hundred. Kate says it is one thousand, four hundred. Sam says it is 14 hundreds. Who is correct? Explain your thinking.

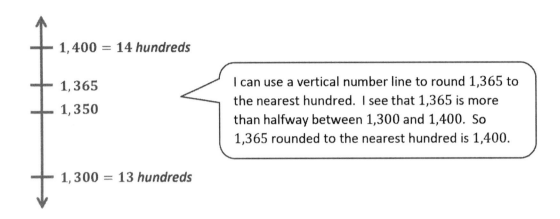

I can use a vertical number line to round 1,365 to the nearest hundred. I see that 1,365 is more than halfway between 1,300 and 1,400. So 1,365 rounded to the nearest hundred is 1,400.

Kate and Sam are both right. 1,365 rounded to the nearest hundred is 1,400. 1,400 in unit form is 14 hundreds.

Lesson 14:   Round to the nearest hundred on the vertical number line.   **EUREKA MATH**

©2015 Great Minds. eureka-math.org
G3-M2-HWH-1.3.0-09.2015

G3-M2-Lesson 15

1. Find the sums below. Choose mental math or the algorithm.

a. 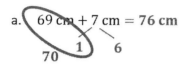 $69 \text{ cm} + 7 \text{ cm} = 76 \text{ cm}$

70   1   6

> I can use mental math to solve this problem. I broke apart the 7 as 1 and 6. Then I solved the equation as $70 \text{ cm} + 6 \text{ cm} = 76 \text{ cm}$.

> For this problem, the standard algorithm is a more strategic tool to use.

b. $59 \text{ kg} + 76 \text{ kg}$

$$
\begin{array}{r}
59 \text{ kg} \\
+\ 76 \text{ kg} \\
\hline
{}_{1} \\
5
\end{array}
$$

$$
\begin{array}{r}
59 \text{ kg} \\
+\ 76 \text{ kg} \\
\hline
{}_{1} \\
135 \text{ kg}
\end{array}
$$

> 9 ones plus 6 ones is 15 ones. I can rename 15 ones as 1 ten and 5 ones. I can record this by writing the 1 so that it crosses the line under the tens in the tens place, and the 5 below the line in the ones column. This way I write 15, rather than 5 and 1 as separate numbers.

> 5 tens plus 7 tens plus 1 ten equals 13 tens. So, $59 \text{ kg} + 76 \text{ kg} = 135 \text{ kg}$.

©2015 Great Minds. eureka-math.org
G3-M2-HWH-1.3.0-09.2015

2. Mrs. Alvarez's plant grew 23 centimeters in one week. The next week it grew 6 centimeters more than the previous week. What is the total number of centimeters the plant grew in 2 weeks?

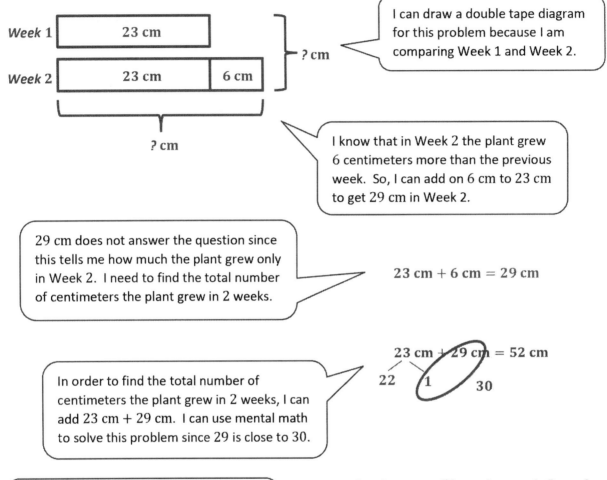

I can draw a double tape diagram for this problem because I am comparing Week 1 and Week 2.

I know that in Week 2 the plant grew 6 centimeters more than the previous week. So, I can add on 6 cm to 23 cm to get 29 cm in Week 2.

29 cm does not answer the question since this tells me how much the plant grew only in Week 2. I need to find the total number of centimeters the plant grew in 2 weeks.

$$23 \text{ cm} + 6 \text{ cm} = 29 \text{ cm}$$

$$23 \text{ cm} + 29 \text{ cm} = 52 \text{ cm}$$
22   1   30

In order to find the total number of centimeters the plant grew in 2 weeks, I can add 23 cm + 29 cm. I can use mental math to solve this problem since 29 is close to 30.

Now I can write a statement that answers the question. This helps me check my work to see if my answer is reasonable.

The plant grew 52 centimeters in 2 weeks.

26   Lesson 15:   Add measurements using the standard algorithm to compose larger
                            units once.

EUREKA
MATH

©2015 Great Minds. eureka-math.org
G3-M2-HWH-1.3.0-09.2015

G3-M2-Lesson 16

1. Find the sums.

a.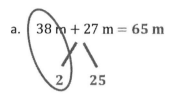

> I can use mental math to solve this problem.
> I can break apart 27 as 2 and 25. Then I can
> solve 40 m + 25 m, which is 65 m.

b. 358 kg + 167 kg

> I can use the standard algorithm to solve this problem. I can line
> the numbers up vertically and add.

$$\begin{array}{r} 385 \text{ kg} \\ +\ 167 \text{ kg} \\ \hline {\scriptstyle 1} \\ 2 \end{array}$$

$$\begin{array}{r} 385 \text{ kg} \\ +\ 167 \text{ kg} \\ \hline {\scriptstyle 11} \\ 52 \end{array}$$

$$\begin{array}{r} 385 \text{ kg} \\ +\ 167 \text{ kg} \\ \hline {\scriptstyle 11} \\ 552 \text{ kg} \end{array}$$

> 5 ones plus 7 ones
> is 12 ones. I can
> rename 12 ones
> as 1 ten 2 ones.

> 8 tens plus 6 tens is
> 14 tens. Plus 1 more
> ten is 15 tens. I can
> rename 15 tens as 1
> hundred 5 tens.

> 3 hundreds plus
> 1 hundred is 4
> hundreds. Plus 1
> more hundred is 5
> hundreds. The
> sum is 552 kg.

2. Matthew reads for 58 more minutes in March than in April. He reads for 378 minutes in April. Use a
    tape diagram to find the total minutes Matthew reads in March and April.

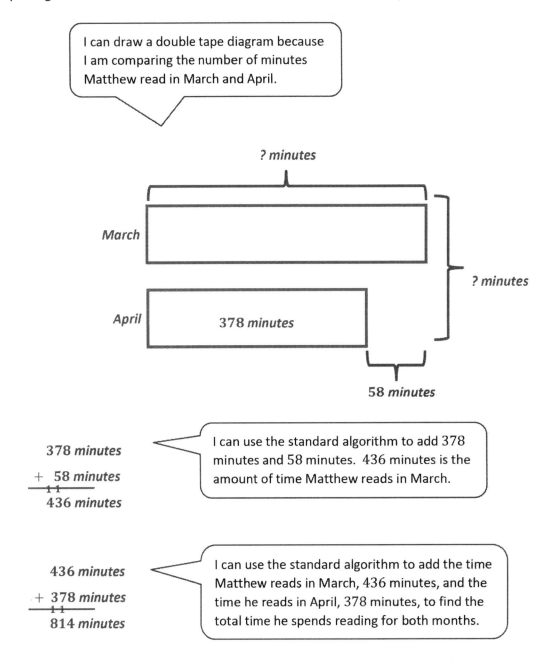

I can draw a double tape diagram because I am comparing the number of minutes Matthew read in March and April.

? minutes

March

? minutes

April   378 minutes

58 minutes

378 *minutes*

+ 58 *minutes*
   1 1
436 *minutes*

I can use the standard algorithm to add 378 minutes and 58 minutes. 436 minutes is the amount of time Matthew reads in March.

436 *minutes*

+ 378 *minutes*
   1 1
814 *minutes*

I can use the standard algorithm to add the time Matthew reads in March, 436 minutes, and the time he reads in April, 378 minutes, to find the total time he spends reading for both months.

Matthew read for 814 minutes in March and April.

Lesson 16:   Add measurements using the standard algorithm to compose larger units twice.   EUREKA
                                                                                                             MATH

©2015 Great Minds. eureka-math.org
G3-M2-HWH-1.3.0-09.2015

G3-M2-Lesson 17

Lucy buys an apple that weighs 152 grams. She buys a banana that weighs 109 grams.

a. Estimate the total weight of the apple and banana by rounding.

$152 \approx 200$
$109 \approx 100$

> I can round each number to the nearest hundred.

$200 \ grams + 100 \ grams = 300 \ grams$

> I can add the rounded numbers to estimate the total weight of the apple and the banana. The total weight is about 300 grams.

b. Estimate the total weight of the apple and banana by rounding in a different way.

$152 \approx 150$
$109 \approx 110$

> I can round each number to the nearest ten.

$150 \ grams + 110 \ grams = 260 \ grams$

> I can add the rounded numbers to estimate the total weight of the apple and the banana. The total weight is about 260 grams.

c. Calculate the actual total weight of the apple and the banana. Which method of rounding was more precise? Why?

$$\begin{array}{r} 152 \ grams \\ + \ 109 \ grams \\ \hline 261 \ grams \end{array}$$

Rounding to the nearest ten grams was more precise because when I rounded to the nearest ten grams, the estimate was 260 grams, and the actual answer is 261 grams. The estimate and the actual answer are only 1 gram apart! When I rounded to the nearest hundred grams, the estimate was 300 grams, which isn't that close to the actual answer.

> I can use the standard algorithm to find the actual total weight of the apple and the banana.

G3-M2-Lesson 18

1. Solve the subtraction problems below.

    a. $50\ cm - 24\ cm\ = \mathbf{26\ cm}$

    > I can use mental math to solve this subtraction problem. I do not have to write it out vertically. I can also think of my work with quarters. I know $50 - 25 = 25$. But since I'm only subtracting 24, I need to add 1 more to 25. So, the answer is 26 cm.

    b. $507\ g - 234\ g$

    $$\begin{array}{r} 507\ g \\ -\ 234\ g \\ \hline \end{array}$$

    > Before I subtract, I need to see if any tens or hundreds need to be unbundled. I can see that there are enough ones to subtract 4 ones from 7 ones. There is no need to unbundle a ten.

    $$\begin{array}{r} {\scriptstyle 4\ 10} \\ \cancel{5}\cancel{0}7\ g \\ -\ 234\ g \\ \hline \end{array}$$

    > But, I am still not ready to subtract. There are not enough tens to subtract 3 tens, so I need to unbundle 1 hundred to make 10 tens. Since I unbundled 1 hundred, there are now 4 hundreds left.

    $$\begin{array}{r} {\scriptstyle 4\ 10} \\ \cancel{5}\cancel{0}7\ g \\ -\ 234\ g \\ \hline 273\ g \end{array}$$

    > After unbundling, I see that there are 4 hundreds, 10 tens, and 7 ones. Now I am ready to subtract. Since I've prepared my numbers all at once, I can subtract left to right, or right to left. The answer is 273 grams.

Lesson 18:   Decompose once to subtract measurements including three-digit
                       minuends with zeros in the tens or ones place.

        ©2015 Great Minds. eureka-math.org
        G3-M2-HWH-1.3.0-09.2015

**EUREKA
MATH**

2. Renee buys 607 grams of cherries at the market on Monday. On Wednesday, she buys 345 grams of cherries. How many more grams of cherries did Renee buy on Monday than on Wednesday?

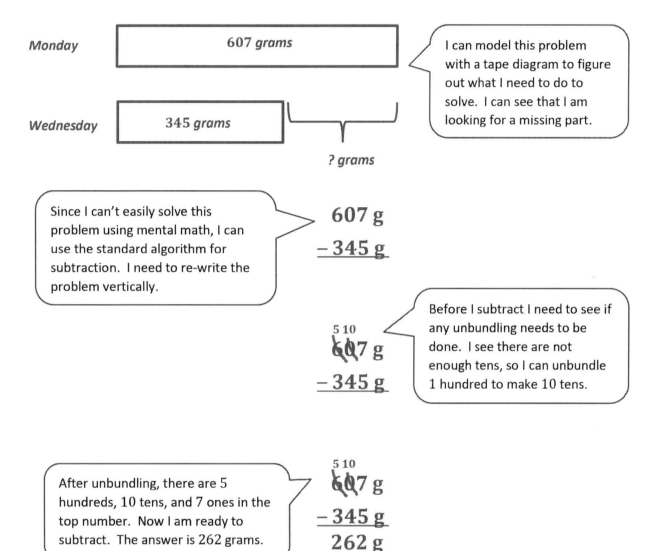

Monday | 607 grams

I can model this problem with a tape diagram to figure out what I need to do to solve. I can see that I am looking for a missing part.

Wednesday | 345 grams

? grams

Since I can't easily solve this problem using mental math, I can use the standard algorithm for subtraction. I need to re-write the problem vertically.

$$607 \text{ g} - 345 \text{ g}$$

Before I subtract I need to see if any unbundling needs to be done. I see there are not enough tens, so I can unbundle 1 hundred to make 10 tens.

⁵ ¹⁰
607 g
− 345 g

After unbundling, there are 5 hundreds, 10 tens, and 7 ones in the top number. Now I am ready to subtract. The answer is 262 grams.

⁵ ¹⁰
607 g
− 345 g
262 g

Renee buys 262 more grams of cherries on Monday than on Wednesday.

EUREKA MATH™   Lesson 18:   Decompose once to subtract measurements including three-digit   31
                            minuends with zeros in the tens or ones place.

©2015 Great Minds. eureka-math.org
G3-M2-HWH-1.3.0-09.2015

G3-M2-Lesson 19

1. Solve the subtraction problems below.

   a. 370 cm − 90 cm = **280 cm**

   > I can use mental math to solve this subtraction problem. I do not have to write it out vertically. Using the compensation strategy, I can add 10 to both numbers and think of the problem as 380 − 100, which is an easy calculation. The answer is 280 cm.

   b. 800 mL − 126 mL

$$\begin{array}{r} {\scriptstyle 7\ 10} \\ \cancel{800}\ \text{mL} \\ -\ 126\ \text{mL} \\ \hline \end{array}$$

   > Before I subtract, I need to see if any tens or hundreds need to be unbundled. There are not enough ones to subtract, so I can unbundle 1 ten to make 10 ones. But there are 0 tens, so I can unbundle 1 hundred to make 10 tens. Then there are 7 hundreds and 10 tens.

$$\begin{array}{r} {\scriptstyle 9} \\ {\scriptstyle 7\ \cancel{10}\,10} \\ \cancel{800}\ \text{mL} \\ -\ 126\ \text{mL} \\ \hline \end{array}$$

   > I still am not ready to subtract because I have to unbundle 1 ten to make 10 ones. Then there are 9 tens and 10 ones.

$$\begin{array}{r} {\scriptstyle 9} \\ {\scriptstyle 7\ \cancel{10}\,10} \\ \cancel{800}\ \text{mL} \\ -\ 126\ \text{mL} \\ \hline 674\ \text{mL} \end{array}$$

   > After unbundling, I see that I have 7 hundreds, 9 tens, and 10 ones. Now I am ready to subtract. Since I've prepared my numbers all at once, I can choose to subtract left to right, or right to left. The answer is 674 mL.

Lesson 19:   Decompose twice to subtract measurements including three-digit minuends with zeros in the tens and ones place.

EUREKA MATH

2. Kenny is driving from Los Angeles to San Diego. The total distance is about 175 kilometers. He has 86 kilometers left to drive. How many kilometers has he driven so far?

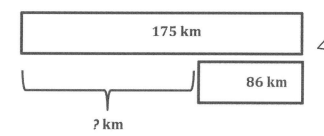

I can model this problem with a tape diagram to figure out what I need to do to solve. I can see that I am looking for a missing part.

Since I can't easily solve this problem using mental math, I can use the standard algorithm for subtraction. I can re-write the problem vertically.

$$\begin{array}{r} 175 \text{ km} \\ -\ 86 \text{ km} \end{array}$$

$$\begin{array}{r} {}^{0\ 17} \\ \cancel{1}\cancel{7}5 \text{ km} \\ -\ 86 \text{ km} \end{array}$$

Before I subtract, I need to see if any unbundling needs to be done. I can see there are not enough tens or ones, so I can unbundle 1 hundred to make 10 tens. After unbundling, there are 0 hundreds and 17 tens.

$$\begin{array}{r} {}^{16} \\ {}^{0\ \cancel{1}7\ 15} \\ \cancel{1}\cancel{7}\cancel{5} \text{ km} \\ -\ 86 \text{ km} \\ \hline 89 \text{ km} \end{array}$$

I can unbundle 1 ten to make 10 ones. After unbundling, there are 0 hundreds, 16 tens, and 15 ones. I am ready to subtract. The answer is 89 kilometers.

Kenny has driven 89 km so far.

©2015 Great Minds. eureka-math.org
G3-M2-HWH-1.3.0-09.2015

G3-M2-Lesson 20

Esther measures rope. She measures a total of 548 centimeters of rope and cuts it into two pieces. The first piece is 152 centimeters long. How long is the second piece of rope?

a. Estimate the length of the second piece of rope by rounding.

$548 \text{ cm} \approx 500 \text{ cm}$

$152 \text{ cm} \approx 200 \text{ cm}$

> I can round each number to the nearest hundred for my first estimate. I notice that both numbers are far from the hundred.

$500 \text{ cm} - 200 \text{ cm} = 300 \text{ cm}$

The second piece of rope is about 300 cm long.

b. Estimate the length of the second piece of ribbon by rounding in a different way.

$548 \text{ cm} \approx 550 \text{ cm}$

$152 \text{ cm} \approx 150 \text{ cm}$

> I can round each number to the nearest ten for my second estimate. Wow, both numbers are close to the fifty! This makes it easy to calculate.

$550 \text{ cm} - 150 \text{ cm} = 400 \text{ cm}$

The second piece of rope is about 400 cm long.

c. Precisely how long is the second piece of rope?

$$\begin{array}{r} {\scriptstyle 4\ 14} \\ \cancel{5}\cancel{4}8 \text{ cm} \\ -\ 152 \text{ cm} \\ \hline 396 \text{ cm} \end{array}$$

> Before I am ready to subtract, I can unbundle 1 hundred for 10 tens.

The second piece of rope is precisely 396 cm long.

34   Lesson 20:   Estimate differences by rounding and apply to solve measurement word   EUREKA
                            problems.   MATH

                        ©2015 Great Minds. eureka-math.org
                        G3-M2-HWH-1.3.0-09.2015

d. Is your answer reasonable? Which estimate was closer to the exact answer?

Rounding to the nearest ten was closer to the exact answer, and it was easy mental math. The estimate was only 4 cm away from the actual answer. So that's how I know my answer is reasonable.

Comparing my actual answer with my estimate helps me check my calculation because if the answers are very different, I've probably made a mistake in my calculation.

EUREKA MATH   Lesson 20:   Estimate differences by rounding and apply to solve measurement word   35
                                 problems.

©2015 Great Minds. eureka-math.org
G3-M2-HWH-1.3.0-09.2015

G3-M2-Lesson 21

Mia measures the lengths of three pieces of wire. The lengths of the wires are recorded to the right.

Wire A	63 cm ≈	__60__ cm
Wire B	75 cm ≈	__80__ cm
Wire C	49 cm ≈	__50__ cm

a. Estimate the total length of Wire A and Wire C. Then, find the actual total length.

> I can round the lengths of all the wires to the nearest ten.

Estimate: $60 \text{ cm} + 50 \text{ cm} = 110 \text{ cm}$

> I can add the rounded lengths of Wires A and C to find an estimate of their total length.

Actual: $63 \text{ cm} + 49 \text{ cm} = 112 \text{ cm}$

$62 \quad 1 \quad 50$

> I can use mental math to solve this problem. I do not have to write it out vertically. I can break apart 63 as 62 and 1. Then I can make the next ten to 50, and then add the 62.

The total length is 112 *cm.*

b. Subtract to estimate the difference between the total length of Wires A and C and the length of Wire B. Then, find the actual difference. Model the problem with a tape diagram.

Estimate: $110 \text{ cm} - 80 \text{ cm} = 30 \text{ cm}$

Actual: $112 \text{ cm} - 75 \text{ cm} = 37 \text{ cm}$

Wire A + Wire C	112 cm
Wire B	75 cm

? cm

> From the tape diagram, I see that I need to solve for an unknown part.

$$\begin{array}{r} \overset{10\ 12}{\cancel{1}\cancel{1}2} \text{ cm} \\ -\ 75 \text{ cm} \\ \hline 37 \text{ cm} \end{array}$$

The difference is 37 *cm.*

> I can write this problem vertically. I can unbundle 1 ten for 10 ones. I can rename 112 as 10 tens and 12 ones. Then I am ready to subtract.

Lesson 21:   Estimate sums and differences of measurements by rounding, and then solve mixed word problems.

EUREKA MATH

Grade 3
Module 3

G3-M3-Lesson 1

1. Write two multiplication facts for each array.

> This array shows 3 rows of 7 dots, or 3 sevens. 3 sevens can be written as $3 \times 7 = 21$. I can also write it as $7 \times 3 = 21$ using the commutative property.

$\underline{21} = \underline{3} \times \underline{7}$

$\underline{21} = \underline{7} \times \underline{3}$

2. Match the expressions.

a. 4×7 6 threes

b.   3 sixes 7×4

> The commutative property says that even if the order of the factors changes, the product stays the same!

3. Complete the equations.

a. $7 \times \underline{2} = \underline{7} \times 2$

$= \underline{14}$

> This equation shows that both sides equal the same amount. Since the factors 7 and 2 are already given, I just have to fill in the unknowns with the correct factors to show that each side equals 14.

b.   6 twos + 2 twos = $\underline{8} \times \underline{2}$

$= \underline{16}$

> This equation shows the break apart and distribute strategy that I learned in Module 1. 6 twos + 2 twos = 8 twos, or 8×2. Since I know $2 \times 8 = 16$, I also know $8 \times 2 = 16$ using commutativity. Using commutativity as a strategy allows me to know many more facts than the ones I've practiced before.

G3-M3-Lesson 2

1. Each has a value of 8.

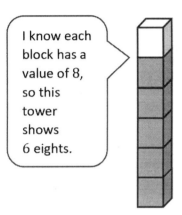

I know each block has a value of 8, so this tower shows 6 eights.

Unit form: 6 eights = __5__ eights + __1__ eight

$$= 40 + \underline{8}$$

$$= \underline{48}$$

The shaded and unshaded blocks show 6 eights broken into 5 eights and 1 eight. These two smaller facts will help me solve the larger fact.

Facts: $\underline{6} \times \underline{8} = \underline{48}$

$\underline{8} \times \underline{6} = \underline{48}$

Using commutativity, I can solve 2 multiplication facts, 6×8 and 8×6, which both equal 48.

2. There are 7 blades on each pinwheel. How many total blades are on 8 pinwheels? Use a fives fact to solve.

I need to find the value of 8×7, or 8 sevens. I can draw a picture. Each dot has a value of 7. I can use my familiar fives facts to break up 8 sevens as 5 sevens and 3 sevens.

$$8 \times 7 = (5 \times 7) + (3 \times 7)$$

$$= 35 + 21$$

$$= 56$$

This is how I write the larger fact as the sum of two smaller facts. I can add their products to find the answer to the larger fact. $8 \times 7 = 56$

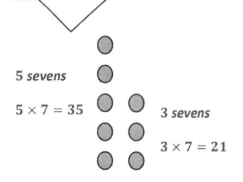

5 *sevens*

$5 \times 7 = 35$

3 *sevens*

$3 \times 7 = 21$

There are 56 blades on 8 pinwheels.

Lesson 2:   Apply the distributive and commutative properties to relate
multiplication facts $5 \times n + n$ to $6 \times n$ and $n \times 6$ where n is the size
of the unit.

©2015 Great Minds. eureka-math.org
G3-M3-HWH-1.3.0-09.2015

**EUREKA
MATH™**

G3-M3-Lesson 3

1. Each equation contains a letter representing the unknown. Find the value of the unknown.

$9 \div 3 = c$	$c = \underline{3}$
$4 \times a = 20$	$a = \underline{5}$

> I can think of this problem as division, $20 \div 4$, to find the unknown factor.

2. Brian buys 4 journals at the store for \$8 each. What is the total amount Brian spends on 4 journals? Use the letter j to represent the total amount Brian spends, and then solve the problem.

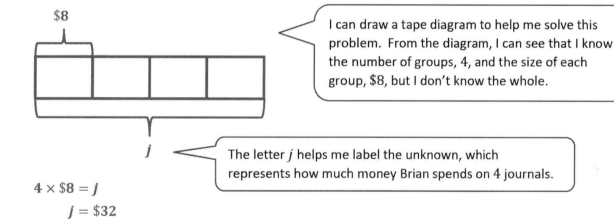

> I can draw a tape diagram to help me solve this problem. From the diagram, I can see that I know the number of groups, 4, and the size of each group, \$8, but I don't know the whole.

> The letter j helps me label the unknown, which represents how much money Brian spends on 4 journals.

$4 \times \$8 = j$

$j = \$32$

Brian spends $\$32$ *on 4 journals.*

> The only thing different about using a letter to solve is that I use the letter to label the unknowns in the tape diagram and in the equation. Other than that, it doesn't change the way I solve. I found the value of j is \$32.

G3-M3-Lesson 4

1. Use number bonds to help you skip-count by six by either making a ten or adding to the ones.

   $60 + 6 = \underline{\quad 66 \quad}$

   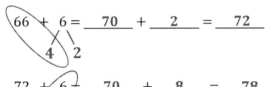

   $66 + 6 = \underline{\quad 70 \quad} + \underline{\quad 2 \quad} = \underline{\quad 72 \quad}$

   $72 + 6 = \underline{\quad 70 \quad} + \underline{\quad 8 \quad} = \underline{\quad 78 \quad}$

   > I can break apart an addend to make a ten. For example, I see that 66 just needs 4 more to make 70. So I can break 6 into 4 and 2. Then $66 + 4 = 70$, plus 2 makes 72. It's much easier to add from a ten. Once I get really good at this, it'll make adding with mental math simple.

2. Count by six to fill in the blanks below.

   $6, \underline{\quad 12 \quad}, \underline{\quad 18 \quad}, \underline{\quad 24 \quad}$

   > I can skip-count to see that 4 sixes make 24.

   Complete the multiplication equation that represents your count-by.

   $6 \times \underline{\quad 4 \quad} = \underline{\quad 24 \quad}$

   > 4 sixes make 24, so $6 \times 4 = 24$.

   Complete the division equation that represents your count-by.

   $\underline{\quad 24 \quad} \div 6 = \underline{\quad 4 \quad}$

   > I'll use a related division fact.
   > $6 \times 4 = 24$, so $24 \div 6 = 4$.

3. Count by six to solve $36 \div 6$. Show your work below.

   $6, 12, 18, 24, 30, 36$

   $36 \div 6 = 6$

   > I'll skip-count by six until I get to 36. Then I can count to find the number of sixes it takes to make 36. It takes 6 sixes, so $36 \div 6 = 6$.

Lesson 4:   Count by units of 6 to multiply and divide using number bonds to decompose.   **EUREKA MATH**

©2015 Great Minds. eureka-math.org
G3-M3-HWH-1.3.0-09.2015

G3-M3-Lesson 5

1. Use number bonds to help you skip-count by seven by either making a ten or adding to the ones.

$70 + 7 = \underline{\quad 77 \quad}$

$\underline{77} + 7 = \underline{\quad 80 \quad} + \underline{\quad 4 \quad} = \underline{\quad 84 \quad}$

3   4

$\underline{84} + 7 = \underline{\quad 90 \quad} + \underline{\quad 1 \quad} = \underline{\quad 91 \quad}$

6   1

> I can break apart an addend to make a ten. For example, I see that 77 just needs 3 more to make 80. So I can break 7 into 3 and 4. Then $77 + 3 = 80$, plus 4 makes 84. It's much easier to add from a ten. Once I get really good at this, it'll make adding with mental math simple.

2. Count by seven to fill in the blanks. Then use the multiplication equation to write the related division fact directly to its right.

$\underline{84}$ $7 \times 12 = \underline{84}$ $\underline{84} \div 7 = \underline{12}$

$\underline{77}$ $7 \times 11 = \underline{77}$ $\underline{77} \div 7 = 11$

> I "climb" the ladder counting by sevens. The count-by helps me find the products of the multiplication facts. First I find the answer to the fact on the bottom rung. I record the answer in the equation and to the left of the ladder. Then I add seven to my answer to find the next number in my count-by. The next number in my count-by is the product of the next fact up on the ladder!

> Once I find the product of a fact by skip-counting, I can write the related division fact. The total, or the product of the multiplication fact, gets divided by 7. The quotient represents the number of sevens I skip-counted.

G3-M3-Lesson 6

1. Label the tape diagram. Then, fill in the blanks below to make the statements true.

$9 \times 8 =$

$(5 \times 8) = \underline{40}$ $(\underline{4} \times 8) = 32$

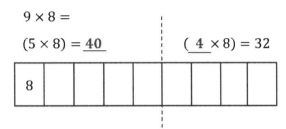

$9 \times 8 = (5 + \underline{4}) \times 8$

$= (5 \times 8) + (\underline{4} \times 8)$

$= \quad 40 \quad + \quad \underline{32}$

$= \quad \underline{72}$

> I can think of 9×8 as 9 eights and break apart the 9 eights into 5 eights and 4 eights. 5 eights equals 40, and 4 eights equals 32. When I add those numbers, I find that 9 eights, or 9×8, equals 72.

2. Break apart 49 to solve $49 \div 7$.

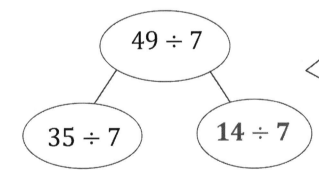

> I can use the break apart and distribute strategy to break 49 apart into 35 and 14. Those are numbers that are easier for me to divide by 7. I know that $35 \div 7 = 5$, and $14 \div 7 = 2$, so $49 \div 7$ equals $5 + 2$, which is 7.

$49 \div 7 = (35 \div 7) + (\underline{14} \div 7)$

$= 5 + \underline{2}$

$= \underline{7}$

Lesson 6:   Use the distributive property as a strategy to multiply and divide using units of 6 and 7.

EUREKA MATH

©2015 Great Minds. eureka-math.org
G3-M3-HWH-1.3.0-09.2015

3. 48 third graders sit in 6 equal rows in the auditorium. How many students sit in each row? Show your thinking.

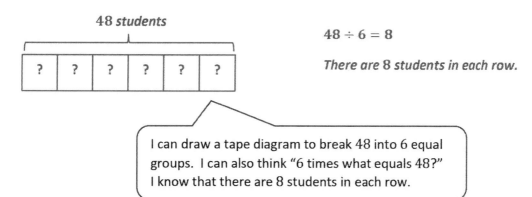

$48 \div 6 = 8$

There are 8 students in each row.

I can draw a tape diagram to break 48 into 6 equal groups. I can also think "6 times what equals 48?" I know that there are 8 students in each row.

4. Ronaldo solves 6×9 by thinking of it as $(5 \times 9) + 9$. Is he correct? Explain Ronaldo's strategy.

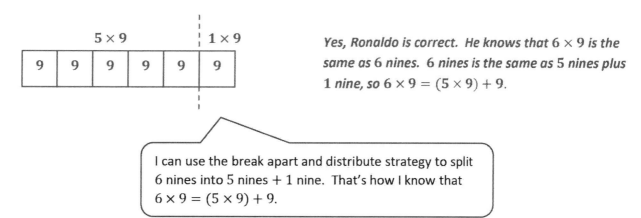

Yes, Ronaldo is correct. He knows that 6×9 is the same as 6 nines. 6 nines is the same as 5 nines plus 1 nine, so $6 \times 9 = (5 \times 9) + 9$.

I can use the break apart and distribute strategy to split 6 nines into 5 nines + 1 nine. That's how I know that $6 \times 9 = (5 \times 9) + 9$.

G3-M3-Lesson 7

1. Match the words on the arrow to the correct equation on the target.

7 times a number equals 56

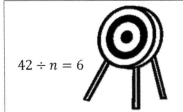

$42 \div n = 6$

The equations use n to represent the unknown number. When I read the words on the left carefully, I can pick out the correct equation on the right.

42 divided by a number equals 6

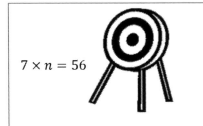

$7 \times n = 56$

2. Ari sells 7 boxes of pens at the school store.

   a. Each box of pens costs $6. Draw a tape diagram, and label the total amount of money Ari makes as m dollars. Write an equation, and solve for m.

   m dollars

   | $6 | $6 | $6 | $6 | $6 | $6 | $6 |

   $7 \times 6 = m$

   $m = 42$

   Ari makes $42 selling pens.

   I'm using the letter m to represent how much money Ari makes. Once I find the value of m, then I know how much money Ari earns selling pens.

Lesson 7:   Interpret the unknown in multiplication and division to model and solve
                                problems using units of 6 and 7.

                        ©2015 Great Minds. eureka-math.org
                        G3-M3-HWH-1.3.0-09.2015

EUREKA
MATH

b. Each box contains 8 pens. Draw a tape diagram, and label the total number of pens as p. Write an equation, and solve for p.

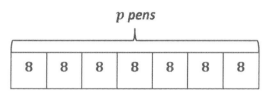

$$7 \times 8 = p$$
$$p = 56$$

Ari sells 56 pens.

I can still use a tape diagram to show the 7 boxes of pens that Ari sells, but this time I'll use the letter p to represent the total number of pens. Since there are 8 pens in each box, I know that the value of p is 56.

3. Mr. Lucas divides 30 students into 6 equal groups for a project. Draw a tape diagram, and label the number of students in each group as n. Write an equation, and solve for n.

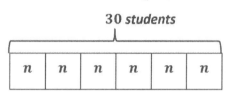

$$30 \div 6 = n$$
$$6 \times n = 30$$
$$n = 5$$

There are 5 students in each group.

I know that 30 students are split into 6 equal groups, so I have to solve $30 \div 6$ to figure out how many students are in each group. I'll use the letter n to represent the unknown. To solve, I can think about this as division or as an unknown factor problem.

EUREKA MATH™   **Lesson 7:**   Interpret the unknown in multiplication and division to model and solve problems using units of 6 and 7.   9

©2015 Great Minds. eureka-math.org
G3-M3-HWH-1.3.0-09.2015

G3-M3-Lesson 8

1. Solve.

    a. $9 - (6 + 3) = \underline{\ \ 0\ \ }$

    b. $(9 - 6) + 3 = \underline{\ \ 6\ \ }$

    > I know the parentheses mean that I have to add $6 + 3$ first. Then I can subtract that sum from 9.

    > I know the parentheses mean that I have to subtract $9 - 6$ first. Then I can add 3. The numbers in parts (a) and (b) are the same, but the answers are different because of where the parentheses are placed.

2. Use parentheses to make the equations true.

    a. $13 = 3 + (5 \times 2)$

    b. $16 = (3 + 5) \times 2$

    > I can put parentheses around 5×2. That means I first multiply 5×2, which equals 10, and then add 3 to get 13.

    > I can put parentheses around $3 + 5$. That means I first add $3 + 5$, which equals 8, and then multiply by 2 to get 16.

3. Determine if the equation is true or false.

    | a. $(4 + 5) \times 2 = 18$ | *True* |
    | b. $5 = 3 + (12 \div 3)$ | *False* |

    > I know part (a) is true because I can add $4 + 5$, which equals 9. Then I can multiply 9×2 to get 18.

    > I know part (b) is false because I can divide 12 by 3, which equals 4. Then I can add $4 + 3$. $4 + 3$ equals 7, not 5.

Lesson 8:   Understand the function of parentheses and apply to solving problems.   **EUREKA MATH**

©2015 Great Minds. eureka-math.org
G3-M3-HWH-1.3.0-09.2015

4. Julie says that the answer to $16 + 10 - 3$ is 23 no matter where she puts the parentheses. Do you agree?

$(16 + 10) - 3 = 23$ $16 + (10 - 3) = 23$

I agree with Julie. I put parentheses around $16 + 10$, and when I solved the equation, I got 23 because $26 - 3 = 23$. Then I moved the parentheses and put them around $10 - 3$. When I subtracted $10 - 3$ first, I still got 23 because $16 + 7 = 23$. Even though I moved the parentheses, the answer didn't change!

Lesson 8:   Understand the function of parentheses and apply to solving problems.   11

©2015 Great Minds. eureka-math.org
G3-M3-HWH-1.3.0-09.2015

G3-M3-Lesson 9

1. Use the array to complete the equation.

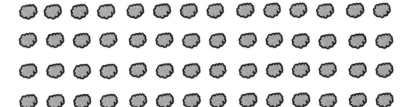

a.   4 × 14 = ___56___

> I can use the array to skip-count by 4 to find the product.

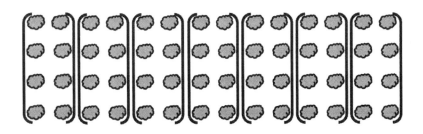

b.   (4 × _2_) × 7

= _8_ × _7_

= _56_

> The array shows that there are 7 groups of 4 × 2.

> I rewrote 14 as 2 × 7. Then I moved the parentheses to make the equation (4 × 2) × 7. I can multiply 4 × 2 to get 8. Then I can multiply 8 × 7 to get 56. Rewriting 14 as 2 × 7 made the problem easier to solve!

2. Place parentheses in the equations to simplify and solve.

$3 \times 21 = 3 \times (3 \times 7)$

$= (3 \times 3) \times 7$ ⎤
$= $ ___63___
$= \underline{\ 9\ } \times 7$ ⎦

> I can put the parentheses around 3 × 3 and then multiply. 3 × 3 equals 9. Now I can solve the easier multiplication fact, 9 × 7.

Lesson 9:   Model the associative property as a strategy to multiply.

EUREKA
MATH

3. Solve. Then, match the related facts.

   a. $24 \times 3 = \underline{\ 72\ } =$ $9 \times (3 \times 2)$

   b. $27 \times 2 = \underline{\ 54\ } =$ $8 \times (3 \times 3)$

I can think of 24 as 8×3. Then, I can move the parentheses to make the new expression $8 \times (3 \times 3)$. $3 \times 3 = 9$, and $8 \times 9 = 72$, so $24 \times 3 = 72$.

I can think of 27 as 9×3. Then, I can move the parentheses to make the new expression $9 \times (3 \times 2)$. $3 \times 2 = 6$, and $9 \times 6 = 54$, so $27 \times 2 = 54$.

©2015 Great Minds. eureka-math.org
G3-M3-HWH-1.3.0-09.2015

G3-M3-Lesson 10

1. Label the array. Then, fill in the blanks to make the statements true.

   $8 \times 6 = 6 \times 8 =$ __48__

   $(6 \times 5) =$ __30__ $(6 \times$ __3__ $) =$ __18__

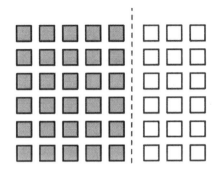

> I can use the array to help me fill in the blanks. The array shows 8 broken into 5 and 3. The shaded part shows $6 \times 5 = 30$, and the unshaded part shows $6 \times 3 = 18$. I can add the products of the smaller arrays to find the total for the entire array. $30 + 18 = 48$, so $8 \times 6 = 48$.

$$8 \times 6 = 6 \times (5 + \underline{\ 3\ })$$
$$= (6 \times 5) + (6 \times \underline{\ 3\ })$$
$$= \ \ 30 \ \ + \ \underline{\ 18\ }$$
$$= \ \underline{\ 48\ }$$

> The equations show the same work that I just did with the array.

2. Break apart and distribute to solve $64 \div 8$.

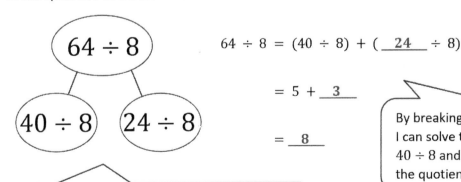

$64 \div 8 = (40 \div 8) + ($ __24__ $\div 8)$

$= 5 +$ __3__

$=$ __8__

> By breaking 64 apart as 40 and 24, I can solve the easier division facts $40 \div 8$ and $24 \div 8$. Then I can add the quotients to solve $64 \div 8$.

> I can use a number bond instead of an array to show how to break apart $64 \div 8$.

Lesson 10:   Use the distributive property as a strategy to multiply and divide.   **EUREKA MATH**

3. Count by 8. Then, match each multiplication problem with its value.

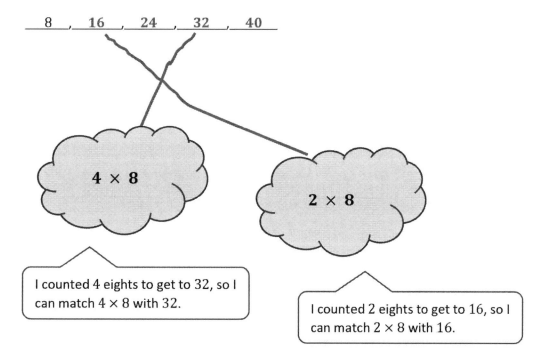

G3-M3-Lesson 11

1. There are 8 pencils in one box. Corey buys 3 boxes. He gives an equal number of pencils to 4 friends. How many pencils does each friend receive?

p

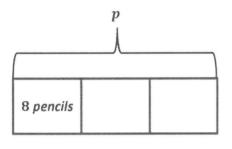

8 pencils

> I can draw a tape diagram to help me solve. I know the number of groups is 3, and the size of each group is 8. I need to solve for the total number of pencils. I can use the letter p to represent the unknown.

$3 \times 8 = p$

$p = 24$

> I can multiply 3×8 to find the total number of pencils Corey buys. Now I need to figure out how many pencils each friend gets.

24 pencils

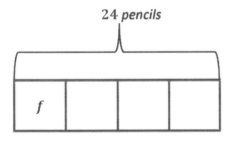

f

> I can draw a tape diagram with 4 units to represent the 4 friends. I know that the total is 24 pencils. I need to solve for the size of each group. I can use the letter f to represent the unknown.

$24 \div 4 = f$

$f = 6$

> I can divide 24 by 4 to find the number of pencils each friend gets.

Each friend receives 6 pencils.

Lesson 11:   Interpret the unknown in multiplication and division to model and solve problems.   **EUREKA MATH**

©2015 Great Minds. eureka-math.org
G3-M3-HWH-1.3.0-09.2015

2. Lilly makes $7 each hour she babysits. She babysits for 8 hours. Lilly uses her babysitting money to buy a toy. After buying the toy, she has $39 left. How much money did Lilly spend on the toy?

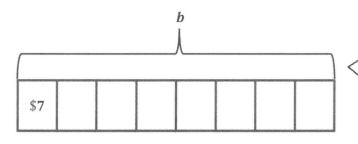

> I can draw a tape diagram to help me solve. I know the number of groups is 8, and the size of each group is $7. I need to solve for the total amount of money. I can use the letter b to represent the unknown.

$8 \times \$7 = b$

$b = \$56$

> I can multiply $8 \times \$7$ to find the total amount of money Lilly earns babysitting. Now I need to figure out how much money she spent on the toy.

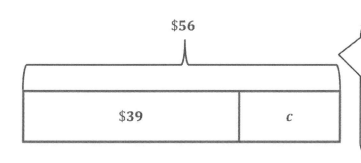

> I can draw a tape diagram with two parts and a total of $56. One part represents the amount of money Lilly has left, $39. The other part is the unknown and represents the amount of money Lilly spent on the toy. I can use the letter c to represent the unknown.

$\$56 - \$39 = c$

> I can subtract $\$56 - \$39$ to find the amount of money Lilly spent on the toy.

$\$57 - \$40 = \$17$

$c = \$17$

> I can use compensation to subtract using mental math. I do that by adding 1 to each number, which makes it easier for me to solve.

$$\begin{array}{r} {\scriptstyle 4\ 16} \\ \$\ \cancel{5}\,\cancel{6} \\ -\ \$\ 3\ 9 \\ \hline \$\ 1\ 7 \end{array}$$

> Or I can use the standard algorithm for subtraction.

Lilly spent $17 on the toy.

EUREKA
MATH™

Lesson 11:   Interpret the unknown in multiplication and division to model and solve
             problems.

17

©2015 Great Minds. eureka-math.org
G3-M3-HWH-1.3.0-09.2015

G3-M3-Lesson 12

1. Each  has a value of 9. Find the value of each row. Then, add the rows to find the total.

$7 \times 9 = \underline{63}$

$5 \times 9 = 45$

$\underline{2} \times 9 = \underline{18}$

> I know each cube has a value of 9. The 2 rows of cubes show 7 nines broken up as 5 nines and 2 nines. It is the break apart and distribute strategy using the familiar fives fact.

$7 \times 9 = (5 + \underline{2}) \times 9$
$= (5 \times 9) + (\underline{2} \times 9)$
$= 45 + \underline{18}$
$= \underline{63}$

> To add 45 and 18, I'll simplify by taking 2 from 45. I'll add the 2 to 18 to make 20. Then I can think of the problem as $43 + 20$.

2. Find the total value of the shaded blocks.

$9 \times 7 =$

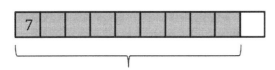

> This shows a different way to solve. I can think of 7 nines as 9 sevens. 9 is closer to 10 than it is to 5. So instead of using a fives fact, I can use a tens fact to solve. I take the product of 10 sevens and subtract 1 seven.

9 sevens = 10 sevens − 1 seven

$= \underline{70} - 7$
$= \underline{63}$

> This strategy made the math simpler and more efficient. I can do $70 - 7$ quickly in my head!

Lesson 12: Apply the distributive property and the fact $9 = 10 - 1$ as a strategy to multiply.

EUREKA MATH

3. James buys a pack of baseball cards. He counts 9 rows of 6 cards. He thinks of 10 sixes to find the total number of cards. Show the strategy that James might have used to find the total number of baseball cards.

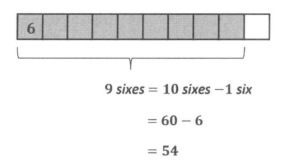

$$9 \; sixes = 10 \; sixes - 1 \; six$$

$$= 60 - 6$$

$$= 54$$

James bought 54 baseball cards.

James uses the tens fact to solve for the nines fact. To solve for 9 sixes, he starts with 10 sixes and subtracts 1 six.

G3-M3-Lesson 13

1. Complete to make true statements.

   a. 10 more than 0 is __10__ ,

      1 less is __9__ .

      $1 \times 9 = $ __9__

   > These statements show a simplifying strategy for skip-counting by nine. It's a pattern of adding 10 and then subtracting 1.

   b. 10 more than 9 is __19__ ,

      1 less is __18__ .

      $2 \times 9 = $ __18__

   > I notice another pattern! I compare the digits in the ones and tens places of the multiples. I can see that from one multiple to the next, the digit in the tens place increases by 1, and the digit in the ones place decreases by 1.

   c. 10 more than 18 is __28__ ,

      1 less is __27__ .

      $3 \times 9 = $ __27__

2.

   a. Analyze the skip-counting strategy in Problem 1. What is the pattern?

   The pattern is add 10 and then subtract 1.

   To get a nines fact, you add 10 and then subtract 1.

   b. Use the pattern to find the next 2 facts. Show your work.

   $4 \times 9 = $ $27 + 10 = 37$ $5 \times 9 = $ $36 + 10 = 46$

                  $37 - 1 = 36$ $46 - 1 = 45$

                  $4 \times 9 = 36$ $5 \times 9 = 45$

   > I can check my answers by adding the digits of each multiple. I know that multiples of 9 I've learned have a sum of digits equal to 9. If the sum isn't equal to 9, I've made a mistake. I know 36 is correct because $3 + 6 = 9$. I know 45 is correct because $4 + 5 = 9$.

Lesson 13:   Identify and use arithmetic patterns to multiply.   **EUREKA MATH**

G3-M3-Lesson 14

1. Tracy figures out the answer to 7×9 by putting down her right index finger (shown). What is the answer? Explain how to use Tracy's finger strategy.

Tracy first lowers the finger that matches the number of nines, 7. She sees that there are 6 fingers to the left of the lowered finger, which is the digit in the tens place, and that there are 3 fingers to the right of the lowered finger, which is the digit in the ones place. So, Tracy's fingers show that the product of 7×9 is 63.

In order for this strategy to work, I have to imagine that my fingers are numbered 1 through 10, with my pinky on the left being number 1 and my pinky on the right being number 10.

2. Chris writes $54 = 9 \times 6$. Is he correct? Explain 3 strategies Chris can use to check his work.

Chris can use the $9 = 10 - 1$ strategy to check his answer.

$$9 \times 6 = (10 \times 6) - (1 \times 6)$$
$$= 60 - 6$$
$$= 54$$

He can also check his answer by finding the sum of the digits in the product to see if it equals 9. Since $5 + 4 = 9$, his answer is correct.

A third strategy for checking his answer is to use the number of groups, 6, to find the digits in the tens place and ones place of the product. He can use $6 - 1 = 5$ to get the digit in the tens place, and $10 - 6 = 4$ to get the digit in the ones place. This strategy also shows that Chris's answer is correct.

Chris can also use the add 10, subtract 1 strategy to list all the nines facts, or he can use the break apart and distribute strategy with fives facts. For example, he can think of 9 sixes as 5 sixes + 4 sixes. There are many strategies and patterns that can help Chris check his work multiplying with nine.

G3-M3-Lesson 15

Judy wants to give each of her friends a bag of 9 marbles. She has a total of 54 marbles. She runs to give them to her friends and gets so excited that she drops and loses 2 bags. How many total marbles does she have left to give away?

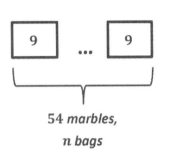

54 *marbles,*

n bags

n represents the number of bags of marbles

$54 \div 9 = n$

$n = 6$

> I can model the problem using a tape diagram. I know Judy has a total of 54 marbles, and each bag has 9 marbles. I don't know how many bags of marbles Judy has at first. Since I know the size of each group is 9 but I don't know the number of groups, I put a "..." in between the 2 units to show that I don't yet know how many groups, or units, to draw.

> I can use the letter n to represent the unknown, which is the number of bags Judy has at first. I can find the unknown by dividing 54 by 9 to get 6 bags. But 6 bags does not answer the question, so my work on this problem is not finished.

> Now I can redraw my model to show the 6 bags of marbles. I know that Judy drops and loses 2 bags. The unknown is the total number of marbles she has left to give away. I can represent this unknown with the letter m.

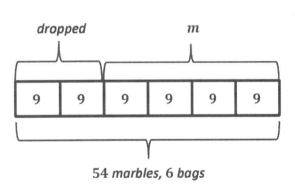

dropped   *m*

54 *marbles, 6 bags*

m represents the total number of marbles left

$4 \times 9 = m$

$m = 36$

Judy still has 36 marbles left to give away.

> From my diagram, I can see that Judy has 4 bags of 9 marbles left. I can choose any of my nines strategies to help me solve 4×9. $4 \times 9 = 36$, which means there are 36 total marbles left.

> I read the problem carefully and made sure to answer with the total number of marbles, not the number of bags. Putting my answer in a statement helps me check that I've answered the problem correctly.

G3-M3-Lesson 16

1. Let $g = 4$. Determine whether the equations are true or false.

a. $g \times 0 = 0$	True
b. $0 \div g = 4$	False
c. $1 \times g = 1$	False
d. $g \div 1 = 4$	True

> I know this equation is false because 0 divided by any number is 0. If I put in any value for g other than 0, the answer will be 0.

> I know this is false because any number times 1 equals that number, not 1. This equation would be correct if it was written as $1 \times g = 4$.

2. Elijah says that any number multiplied by 1 equals that number.

   a. Write a multiplication equation using c to represent Elijah's statement.

   $1 \times c = c$

   > I can also use the commutative property to write my equation as $c \times 1 = c$.

   b. Using your equation from part (a), let $c = 6$, and draw a picture to show that the new equation is true.

   > My picture shows 1 group multiplied by c, or 6. 1 group of 6 makes a total of 6. This works for any value, not just 6.

EUREKA MATH   Lesson 16:   Reason about and explain arithmetic patterns using units of 0 and 1 as they relate to multiplication and division.   23

©2015 Great Minds. eureka-math.org
G3-M3-HWH-1.3.0-09.2015

G3-M3-Lesson 17

1. Explain how $8 \times 7 = (5 \times 7) + (3 \times 7)$ is shown in the multiplication table.

    The multiplication table shows $5 \times 7 = 35$ and $3 \times 7 = 21$. So, $35 + 21 = 56$, which is the product of 8×7.

    > This is the break apart and distribute strategy. Using that strategy, I can add the products of 2 smaller facts to find the product of a larger fact.

2. Use what you know to find the product of 3×16.

    $3 \times 16 = (3 \times 8) + (3 \times 8)$
    $\qquad = 24 + 24$
    $\qquad = 48$

    > I can also break up 3×16 as 10 threes + 6 threes, which is $30 + 18$. Or I can add 16 three times: $16 + 16 + 16$. I always want to use the most efficient strategy. This time it helped me to see the problem as double 24.

3. Today in class we found that $n \times n$ is the sum of the first n odd numbers. Use this pattern to find the value of n for each equation below.

    a. $1 + 3 + 5 = n \times n$
        $9 = 3 \times 3$

    > The sum of the first 3 odd numbers is the same as the product of 3×3. The sum of the first 4 odd numbers is the same as the product of 4×4. The sum of the first 5 odd numbers is the same as the product of 5×5.

    b. $1 + 3 + 5 + 7 = n \times n$
        $16 = 4 \times 4$

    c. $1 + 3 + 5 + 7 + 9 = n \times n$
        $25 = 5 \times 5$

    > Wow, it's a pattern! I know that the first 6 odd numbers will be the same as the product of 6×6 and so on.

Lesson 17:   Identify patterns in multiplication and division facts using the
                          multiplication table.

EUREKA
MATH

G3-M3-Lesson 18

William has $187 in the bank. He saves the same amount of money each week for 6 weeks and puts it in the bank. Now William has $241 in the bank. How much money does William save each week?

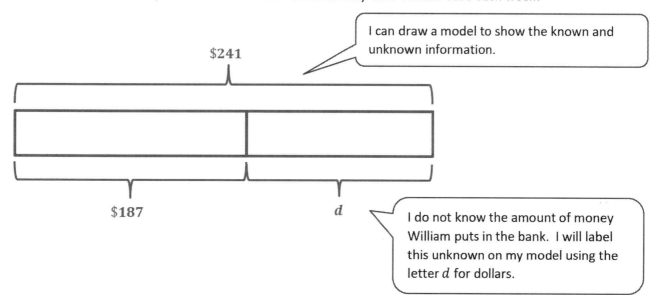

$241

I can draw a model to show the known and unknown information.

$187 d

I do not know the amount of money William puts in the bank. I will label this unknown on my model using the letter d for dollars.

d represents the number of dollars William puts in the bank

$$\$241 - \$187 = d$$
$$d = \$54$$

I can write what d represents and then write an equation to solve for d. I can subtract the known part, $187, from the whole amount, $241, to find d.

This answer is reasonable because $187 + $54 = $241. But it does not answer the question the problem asks. I'm trying to figure out how much money William saves each week, so I need to adjust my model.

EUREKA MATH

Lesson 18: Solve two-step word problems involving all four operations and assess the reasonableness of solutions.

25

©2015 Great Minds. eureka-math.org
G3-M3-HWH-1.3.0-09.2015

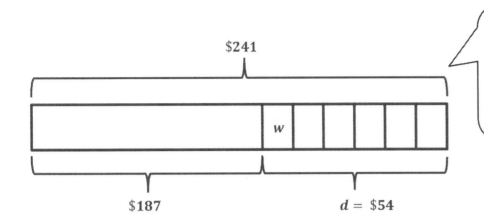

$241

$187 $d = 54

w represents the number of dollars saved each week

$54 ÷ 6 = w$

$w = 9

I will write what w represents and then write an equation to solve for w. I can divide $54 by 6 to get $9.

William saves $9 each week.

My answer is reasonable because $9 a week for 6 weeks is $54. That's about $50. $187 is about $190. $190 + $50 = $240, which is very close to $241. My estimate is only $1 less than my answer!

I can explain why my answer is reasonable by estimating.

EUREKA
MATH

G3-M3-Lesson 19

1. Use the disks to fill in the blanks in the equations.

This array of disks shows 2 rows of 3 ones.

This array of disks shows 2 rows of 3 tens.

a.

2×3 ones = ___6___ ones

$2 \times 3 =$ ___6___

b.

2×3 tens = ___6___ tens

$2 \times 30 =$ ___60___

The top equations are written in unit form. The bottom equations are written in standard form. The 2 equations say the same thing.

I see that both arrays have the same number of disks. The only difference is the unit. The array on the left uses ones, and the array on the right uses tens.

I see that the difference between Problems 1 and 2 is the model. Problem 1 uses place value disks. Problem 2 uses the chip model. With both models, I'm still multiplying ones and tens.

2. Use the chart to complete the blanks in the equations.

tens	ones
	● ● ● ●
	● ● ● ●
	● ● ● ●

tens	ones
● ● ● ●	
● ● ● ●	
● ● ● ●	

a. 3×4 ones = __12__ ones

3×4 = __12__

b. 3×4 tens = __12__ tens

3×40 = __120__

I notice the number of dots is exactly the same in both charts. The difference between the charts is that when the units change from ones to tens, the dots shift over to the tens place.

3. Match.

80 × 2 ———————— 160

In order to solve a more complicated problem like this one, I can first think of it as 8 ones × 2, which is 16. Then all I need to do is move the answer over to the tens place so it becomes 16 tens. 16 tens is the same as 160.

Lesson 19: Multiply by multiples of ten using the place value chart.

EUREKA MATH

G3-M3-Lesson 20

1. Use the chart to complete the equations. Then solve.

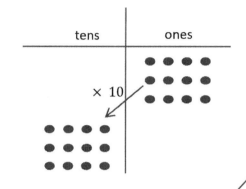

> I know that parentheses change the way numbers are grouped for solving. I can see that the parentheses group 3×4 ones, so I'll do that part of the equation first. 3×4 ones $= 12$ ones. Next I'll multiply the 12 ones by 10. The equation becomes $12 \times 10 = 120$. The chip model shows how I can multiply the 3 groups of 4 ones by 10.

a. $(3 \times 4) \times 10$

$= (12 \text{ ones}) \times 10$

$= \underline{\quad 120 \quad}$

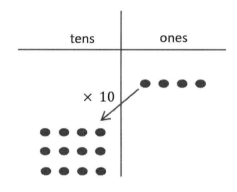

> I can see that here the parentheses move over and group the 4 ones $\times$ 10. I'll solve that first to get 40, or 4 tens. Then I can multiply the 4 tens by 3. So the equation becomes $3 \times 40 = 120$. The chip model shows how I multiply 4 ones by 10 first and then multiply the 4 tens by three.

b. $3 \times (4 \times 10)$

$= 3 \times (4 \text{ tens})$

$= \underline{\quad 120 \quad}$

> By moving the parentheses over and grouping the numbers differently, this problem becomes friendlier. 3×40 is a little easier than multiplying 12×10. This new strategy will me help find larger unknown facts later on.

EUREKA MATH   Lesson 20:   Use place value strategies and the associative property $n \times (m \times 10) = (n \times m) \times 10$ **29**
(where n and m are less than 10) to multiply multiples of 10.

©2015 Great Minds. eureka-math.org
G3-M3-HWH-1.3.0-09.2015

2. John solves 30×3 by thinking about 10×9. Explain his strategy.

$$
\begin{aligned}
30 \times 3 &= (10 \times 3) \times 3 \\
&= 10 \times (3 \times 3) \\
&= 10 \times 9 \\
&= 90
\end{aligned}
$$

John writes 30×3 as $(10 \times 3) \times 3$. Then he moves the parentheses over to group 3×3. Solving 3×3 first makes the problem easier. Instead of 30×3, John can solve by thinking of an easier fact, 10×9.

Although it is easy to solve for 30×3, John moves the parentheses over and groups the numbers differently to make the problem a little friendlier for him. It's just another way to think about the problem.

Lesson 20: Use place value strategies and the associative property $n \times (m \times 10) = (n \times m) \times$ (where n and m are less than 10) to multiply multiples of 10.

EUREKA MATH

G3-M3-Lesson 21

Jen makes 34 bracelets. She gives 19 bracelets away as gifts and sells the rest for $3 each. She would like to buy an art set that costs $55 with the money she earns. Does she have enough money to buy it? Explain why or why not.

> I can draw a model to show the known and unknown information. I can see from my drawing that I need to find a missing part. I can label my missing part with a b to represent the number of bracelets Jen has left to sell.

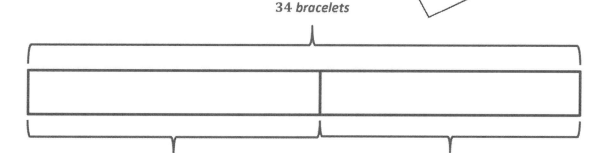

34 bracelets

19 bracelets   b bracelets

b represents the number of bracelets Jen has left to sell

$34 - 19 = b$

$\qquad b = 15$

> I can write what b represents and then write an equation to solve for b. I subtract the given part, 19, from the whole amount, 34. I can use a compensation strategy to think of $34 - 19$ as $35 - 20$ because $35 - 20$ is an easier fact to solve. Jen has 15 bracelets left.

> This answer is reasonable because $19 + 15 = 34$. But it doesn't answer the question in the problem. Next, I have to figure out how much money Jen earns from selling the 15 bracelets, so I need to adjust my model.

EUREKA MATH™   **Lesson 21:**   Solve two-step word problems involving multiplying single-digit factors and multiplies of 10.   31

©2015 Great Minds. eureka-math.org
G3-M3-HWH-1.3.0-09.2015

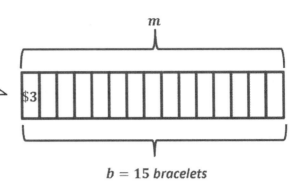

Now that I know Jen has 15 bracelets left, I can split this part into 15 smaller equal parts. I know that she sells each bracelet for $3, so each part has a value of $3. I can also label the unknown as m to represent how much money Jen earns in total.

$b = 15$ *bracelets*

m represents the amount of money Jen earns

$15 \times 3 = m$

$\quad m = (10 \times 3) + (5 \times 3)$

$\quad m = 30 + 15$

$\quad m = 45$

I can write what m represents and then write an equation to solve for m. I need to multiply 15 by 3, a large fact! I can use the break apart and distribute strategy to solve for 15×3. I can break up 15 threes as 10 threes and 5 threes and then find the sum of the 2 smaller facts.

Jen earns a total of $45 *from selling* 15 *bracelets.*

Jen does not have enough money to buy the art set. She is $10 *short.*

I am not finished answering the question until I explain why Jen does not have enough money to buy the art set.

32   Lesson 21:   Solve two-step word problems involving multiplying single-digit factors
                                and multiples of 10.

©2015 Great Minds. eureka-math.org
G3-M3-HWH-1.3.0-09.2015

EUREKA
MATH

Homework Helpers

Grade 3
Module 4

G3-M4-Lesson 1

1. Vivian uses squares to find the area of a rectangle. Her work is shown below.

    a. How many squares did she use to cover the rectangle?

    > I know that the amount of flat space a shape takes up is called its area.

    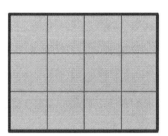

    > I know these are called square units because the units used to measure area are squares. I also know that to measure area there shouldn't be any gaps or overlaps.

    _____12_____ squares

    b. What is the area of the rectangle in square units? Explain how you found your answer.

    The area of the rectangle is 12 square units. I know because I counted 12 squares inside the rectangle.

2. Each is 1 square unit. Which rectangle has the largest area? How do you know?

    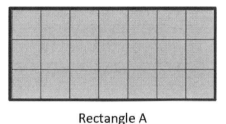

    Rectangle A

    21 *square units*

    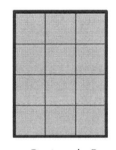

    > I can compare the areas of these rectangles because the same-sized square unit is used to cover each one.

    Rectangle B

    12 *square units*

    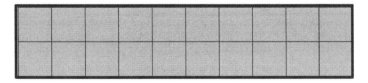

    Rectangle C

    20 *square units*

    Rectangle A has the largest area. I know because I counted the square units in each rectangle. Rectangle A needs the most squares to cover it with no gaps or overlaps.

G3-M4-Lesson 2

1. Matthew uses square inches to create these rectangles. Do they have the same area? Explain.

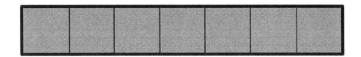

7 *square inches*

8 *square inches*

No, they do not have the same area. I counted the square inches in each rectangle and found that the rectangle on the right has a larger area by 1 square inch.

> This is the new unit I learned today. Each side of a square inch measures 1 inch. The units in this drawing are just meant to represent square inches. I can write square inches as sq in for short.

2. Each ⬜ is a square unit. Count to find the area of the rectangle below. Then, draw a different rectangle that has the same area.

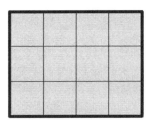

12 *square units*

12 *square units*

> I can rearrange the 12 square units into two equal rows to make a new rectangle. I know that rearranging the square units does not change the area because no new units are added, and none are taken away.

Lesson 2:   Decompose and recompose shapes to compare areas.

©2015 Great Minds. eureka-math.org
G3-M4-HWH-1.3.0-10.2015

EUREKA MATH

G3-M4-Lesson 3

1. Each is 1 square unit. What is the area of each of the following rectangles?

    a.

    ___6 square units___

    I can find the area of each rectangle by counting the number of square units.

    b.

    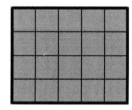

    ___20 square units___

2. How would the rectangles in Problem 1 be different if they were composed of square inches?

    The number of squares in each rectangle would stay the same, but the side of each square would measure 1 inch. We would also label the area as square inches instead of square units.

    I know 1 square inch covers a greater area than 1 square centimeter because 1 inch is longer than 1 centimeter.

3. How would the rectangles in Problem 1 be different if they were composed of square centimeters?

    The number of squares in each rectangle would stay the same, but the side of each square would measure 1 centimeter. We would also label the area as square centimeters instead of square units.

     Lesson 3:   Model tiling with centimeter and inch unit squares as a strategy to
                       measure area.

©2015 Great Minds. eureka-math.org
G3-M4-HWH-1.3.0-10.2015   3

G3-M4-Lesson 4

1. Use a ruler to measure the side lengths of the rectangle in centimeters. Mark each centimeter with a point, and draw lines from the points to show the square units. Then, count the squares you drew to find the total area.

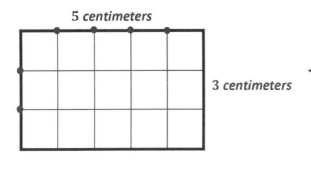

5 centimeters

3 centimeters

> I know the side length of a rectangle is the same as the number of centimeter tiles that make it. I also know that opposite sides of rectangles are equal, so I only need to measure 2 sides.

Total area: __15 square centimeters__

2. Each ☐ is 1 square centimeter. Sammy says that the side length of the rectangle below is 8 centimeters. Davis says the side length is 3 centimeters. Who is correct? Explain how you know.

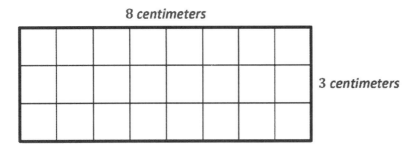

8 centimeters

3 centimeters

> An efficient strategy to find the area is to think of this rectangle as 3 rows of 8 tiles, or 3 eights. Then we can skip-count by eights 3 times to find the total number of square centimeter tiles.

They are both correct because I counted the tiles across the top, and there are 8 tiles, which means that the side length is 8 cm. Then I counted the tiles along the side, and there are 3 tiles, which means that the side length is 3 cm.

EUREKA MATH

3. Shana uses square inch tiles to find the side lengths of the rectangle below. Label each side length. Then, find the total area.

5 *inches*

2 *inches*

Total area: ___10 *square inches*___

> I know the units are labeled differently for side lengths and area. I know the unit for side lengths is inches because the unit measures the length of the side in inches. For area, the unit is square inches because I count the number of square inch tiles that are used to make the rectangle.

4. How does knowing side lengths W and X help you find side lengths Y and Z on the rectangle below?

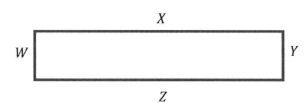

I know that opposite sides of a rectangle are equal. So, if I know side length X, I also know side length Z. If I know side length W, I also know side length Y.

G3-M4-Lesson 5

1. Use the centimeter side of a ruler to draw in the tiles. Then, find and label the unknown side length. Skip-count the tiles to check your work. Write a multiplication sentence for each tiled rectangle.

   a. Area: 12 square centimeters

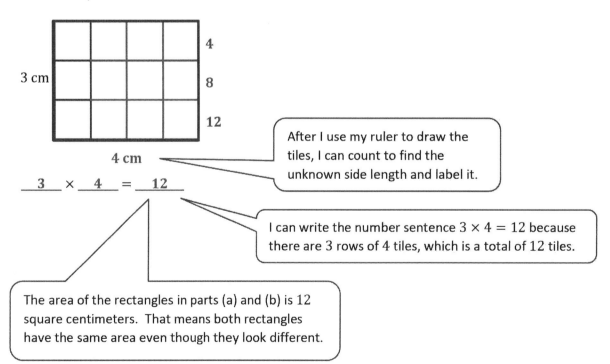

   I can use my ruler to mark each centimeter. Then, I can connect the marks to draw the tiles. I'll count the square units and label the unknown side length 3 cm.

   Next, I'll skip-count by 3 to check that the total number of tiles matches the given area of 12 square centimeters.

   $$\underline{4} \times \underline{3} = \underline{12}$$

   I can write 3 for the unknown factor because my tiled array shows 4 rows of 3 tiles.

   b. Area: 12 square centimeters

   $$\underline{3} \times \underline{4} = \underline{12}$$

   After I use my ruler to draw the tiles, I can count to find the unknown side length and label it.

   I can write the number sentence $3 \times 4 = 12$ because there are 3 rows of 4 tiles, which is a total of 12 tiles.

   The area of the rectangles in parts (a) and (b) is 12 square centimeters. That means both rectangles have the same area even though they look different.

EUREKA
MATH

2. Ella makes a rectangle with 24 square centimeter tiles. There are 4 equal rows of tiles.

    a. How many tiles are in each row? Use words, pictures, and numbers to support your answer.

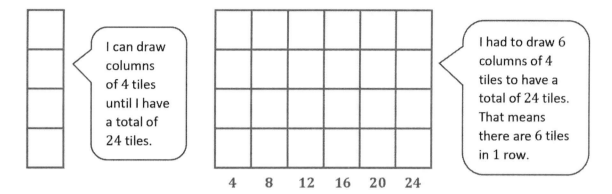

There are 6 tiles in each row. I drew columns of 4 tiles until I had a total of 24 tiles. Then I counted how many tiles are in 1 row. I could also find the answer by thinking about the problem as 4 × _____ = 24 because I know that 4 × 6 = 24.

    b. Can Ella arrange all of her 24 square centimeter tiles into 3 equal rows? Use words, pictures, and numbers to support your answer.

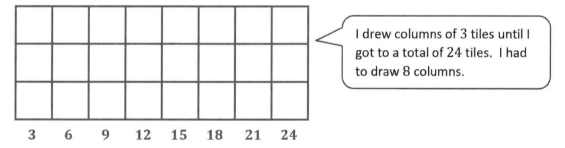

Yes, Ella can arrange all of her 24 tiles into 3 equal rows. I drew columns of 3 tiles until I had a total of 24 tiles. I can use my picture to see that there are 8 tiles in each row. I can also use multiplication to help me because I know that 3 × 8 = 24.

    c. Do the rectangles in parts (a) and (b) have the same total area? Explain how you know.

Yes, the rectangles in parts (a) and (b) have the same area because they are both made up of 24 square centimeter tiles. The rectangles look different because they have different side lengths, but they have the same area.

> This is different than Problem 1 because the rectangles in Problem 1 had the same side lengths. They were just rotated.

G3-M4-Lesson 6

1. Each ☐ represents 1 square centimeter. Draw to find the number of rows and columns in each array. Match it to its completed array. Then, fill in the blanks to make a true equation to find each array's area.

a.

b.

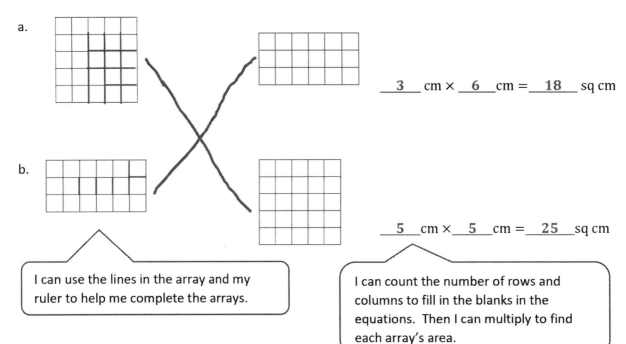

___3___ cm × ___6___ cm = ___18___ sq cm

___5___ cm × ___5___ cm = ___25___ sq cm

I can use the lines in the array and my ruler to help me complete the arrays.

I can count the number of rows and columns to fill in the blanks in the equations. Then I can multiply to find each array's area.

2. A painting covers the tile wall in Ava's kitchen, as shown below.

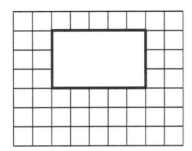

a. Ava skip-counts by 9 to find the total number of square tiles on the wall. She says there are 63 square tiles. Is she correct? Explain your answer.

Yes, Ava is correct. Even though I can't see all of the tiles, I can use the first row and column to see that there are 7 rows of 9 tiles. I can multiply 7 × 9, which equals 63.

Lesson 6:   Draw rows and columns to determine the area of a rectangle given an incomplete array.

©2015 Great Minds. eureka-math.org
G3-M4-HWH-1.3.0-10.2015

EUREKA MATH™

b. How many square tiles are under the painting?

I can use the tiles around the painting to help me figure out how many tiles are under the painting.

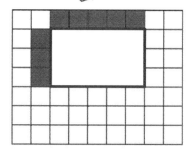

$3 \times 5 = 15$ There are 3 rows of square tiles and 5 columns of square tiles under the painting. I can multiply 3×5 to find the total number of tiles under the painting.

$63 - 48 = 15$ I know from part (a) that there are 63 total tiles. So, I could also solve by subtracting the number of tiles that I can see from the total.

There are 15 *square tiles under the painting.*

G3-M4-Lesson 7

1. Find the area of the rectangular array. Label the side lengths of the matching area model, and write a multiplication equation for the area model.

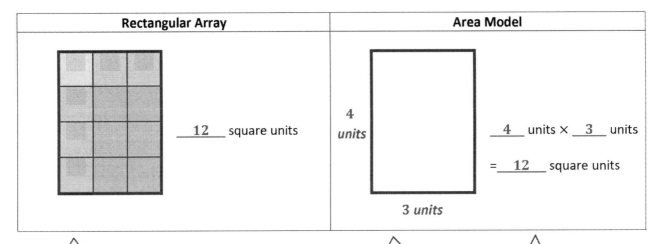

Rectangular Array	Area Model
__12__ square units	4 units ... 3 units __4__ units × __3__ units = __12__ square units

I can skip-count rows by 3 or columns by 4 to find the area of the rectangular array.

I can use the rectangular array to help me label the side lengths of the area model. There are 4 rows, so the width is 4 units. There are 3 columns, so the length is 3 units.

I can multiply 4 × 3 to find the area. The area model and the rectangular array have the same area of 12 square units.

2. Mason arranges square pattern blocks into a 3 by 6 array. Draw Mason's array on the the grid below. How many square units are in Mason's rectangular array?

a.

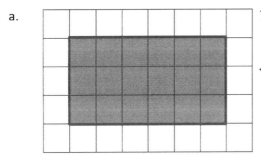

There are 18 square units in Mason's rectangular array.

I can draw a rectangular array with 3 rows and 6 columns. Then I can multiply 3 × 6 to find the total number of square units in the rectangular array.

©2015 Great Minds. eureka-math.org
G3-M4-HWH-1.3.0-10.2015

b. Label the side lengths of Mason's array from part (a) on the rectangle below. Then, write a multiplication sentence to represent the area of the rectangle.

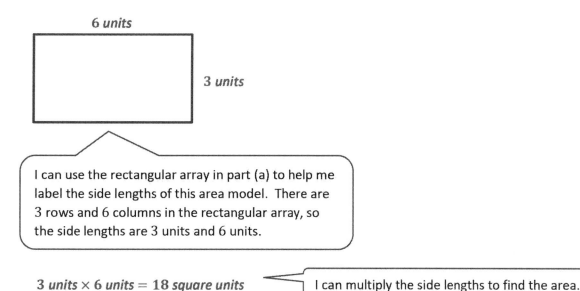

6 *units*

3 *units*

I can use the rectangular array in part (a) to help me label the side lengths of this area model. There are 3 rows and 6 columns in the rectangular array, so the side lengths are 3 units and 6 units.

3 *units* × 6 *units* = 18 *square units*

I can multiply the side lengths to find the area.

3. Luke draws a rectangle that is 4 square feet. Savannah draws a rectangle that is 4 square inches. Whose rectangle is larger in area? How do you know?

Luke's rectangle is larger in area because they both used the same number of units, but the size of the units is different. Luke used square feet, which are larger than square inches. Since the units that Luke used are larger than the units that Savannah used and they both used the same number of units, Luke's rectangle is larger in area.

I can think about the lesson today to help me answer this question. My partner and I made rectangles using square inch and square centimeter tiles. We both used the same number of tiles to make our rectangles, but we noticed that the rectangle made of square inches was larger in area than the rectangle made of square centimeters. The larger unit, square inches, made a rectangle with a larger area.

EUREKA MATH™

Lesson 7: Interpret area models to form rectangular arrays.

11

©2015 Great Minds. eureka-math.org
G3-M4-HWH-1.3.0-10.2015

G3-M4-Lesson 8

1. Write a multiplication equation to find the area of the rectangle.

8 cm

4 cm   Area: __32__ sq cm

> I know that I can multiply the side lengths, 4 and 8, to find the area.

__4__ × __8__ = __32__

2. Write a multiplication equation and a division equation to find the unknown side length for the rectangle.

__9__ ft

2 ft   Area: 18 sq ft

> To solve, I can think of this as multiplication with an unknown factor, $2 \times$ ____ $= 18$. Or, I can divide the area by the known side length, $18 \div 2 =$ ____. Either way, the answer is 9.

__2__ × __9__ = __18__

__18__ ÷ __2__ = __9__

3. On the grid below, draw a rectangle that has an area of 24 square units. Label the side lengths.

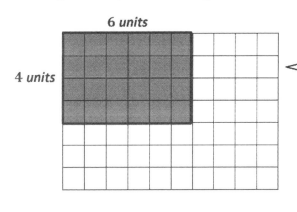

6 units

4 units

> To draw a rectangle with an area of 24 square units, I can think about factors of 24. I know $4 \times 6 = 24$, so my side lengths can be 4 and 6.

4. Keith draws a rectangle that has side lengths of 6 inches and 3 inches. What is the area of the rectangle?
    Explain how you found your answer.

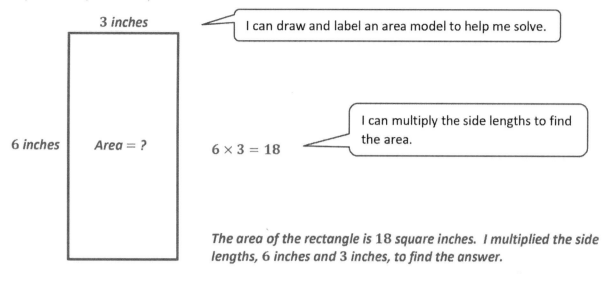

I can draw and label an area model to help me solve.

I can multiply the side lengths to find the area.

$6 \times 3 = 18$

The area of the rectangle is 18 square inches. I multiplied the side lengths, 6 inches and 3 inches, to find the answer.

5. Isabelle draws a rectangle with a side length of 5 centimeters and an area of 30 square centimeters.
    What is the other side length? How do you know?

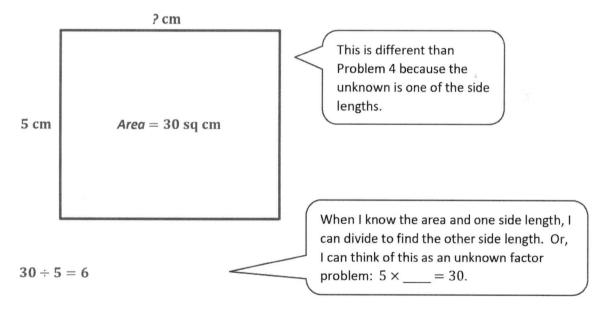

This is different than Problem 4 because the unknown is one of the side lengths.

When I know the area and one side length, I can divide to find the other side length. Or, I can think of this as an unknown factor problem: $5 \times \underline{\quad} = 30$.

$30 \div 5 = 6$

The other side length is 6 centimeters. I divided the area, 30 square centimeters, by the known side length, 5 centimeters, and $30 \div 5 = 6$.

©2015 Great Minds. eureka-math.org
G3-M4-HWH-1.3.0-10.2015

G3-M4-Lesson 9

1. Use the grid to answer the questions below.

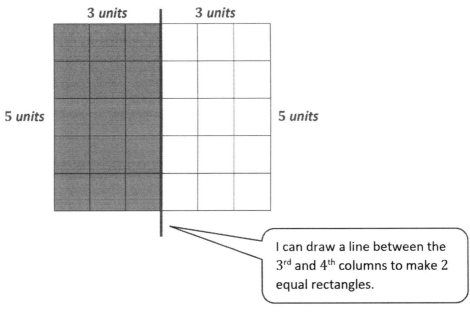

3 units | 3 units

5 units   5 units

> I can draw a line between the 3rd and 4th columns to make 2 equal rectangles.

a. Draw a line to divide the grid into 2 equal rectangles. Shade in 1 of the rectangles that you created.

b. Label the side lengths of each rectangle.

> I can count the units on each side to help me label the side lengths of each rectangle.

c. Write an equation to show the total area of the 2 rectangles.

$Area = (5 \times 3) + (5 \times 3)$
$\quad\;\; = 15 + 15$
$\quad\;\; = 30$

The total area is 30 square units.

> I can find the area of each smaller rectangle by multiplying 5×3. Then, I can add the areas of the 2 equal rectangles to find the total area.

14   Lesson 9:   Analyze different rectangles and reason about their area.

EUREKA MATH

©2015 Great Minds. eureka-math.org
G3-M4-HWH-1.3.0-10.2015

2. Phoebe cuts out the 2 equal rectangles from Problem 1(a) and puts the two shorter sides together.

    a. Draw Phoebe's new rectangle, and label the side lengths below.

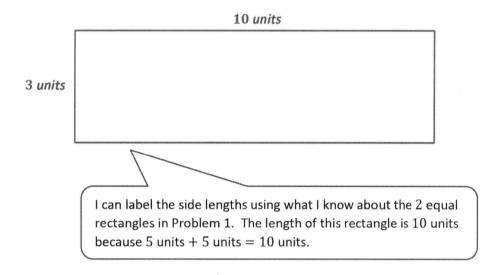

10 *units*

3 *units*

I can label the side lengths using what I know about the 2 equal rectangles in Problem 1. The length of this rectangle is 10 units because 5 units + 5 units = 10 units.

    b. Find the total area of the new, longer rectangle.

$Area = 3 \times 10$
$\quad\quad = 30$
The total area is 30 *square units.*

I can find the area by multiplying the side lengths.

    c. Is the area of the new, longer rectangle equal to the total area in Problem 1(c)? Explain why or why not.

Yes, the area of the new, longer rectangle is equal to the total area in Problem 1(c). Phoebe just rearranged the 2 smaller, equal rectangles, so the total area didn't change.

I know that the total area doesn't change just because the 2 equal rectangles were moved around to form a new, longer rectangle. No units were taken away and none were added, so the area stays the same.

G3-M4-Lesson 10

1. Label the side lengths of the shaded and unshaded rectangles. Then, find the total area of the large rectangle by adding the areas of the 2 smaller rectangles.

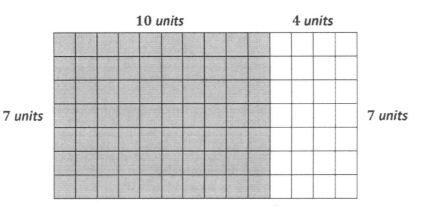

$7 \times 14 = 7 \times ($ ___10___ $+$ __4__ $)$

$ = (7 \times$ ___10___ $) + (7 \times$ __4__ $)$

$ =$ __70__ $+$ __28__

$ =$ __98__

Area: ___98___ square units

> I can count the units on each side to help me label the side lengths of each rectangle.

Lesson 10:   Apply the distributive property as a strategy to find the total area of a large rectangle by adding two products.

©2015 Great Minds. eureka-math.org
G3-M4-HWH-1.3.0-10.2015

EUREKA MATH

2. Vickie imagines 1 more row of seven to find the total area of a 9×7 rectangle. Explain how this could help her solve 9×7.

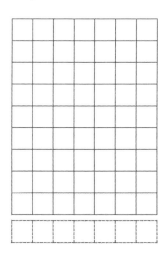

This can help her solve 9×7 because now she can think of it as 10×7 minus 1 seven. 10×7 might be easier for Vickie to solve than 9×7.

$10 \times 7 = 70$

$70 - 7 = 63$

This reminds me of the $9 = 10 - 1$ strategy that I can use to multiply by 9.

3. Break the 16×6 rectangle into 2 rectangles by shading one smaller rectangle within it. Then, find the total area by finding the sum of the areas of the 2 smaller rectangles. Explain your thinking.

6 units

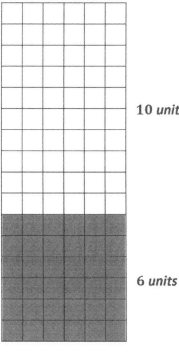

10 units

6 units

Area $= (10 \times 6) + (6 \times 6)$

$= 60 + 36$

$= 96$

The total area is 96 square units.

I broke apart the 16×6 rectangle into 2 smaller rectangles: 10×6 and 6×6. I chose to break it apart like this because those are easy facts for me. I multiplied the side lengths to find the area of each smaller rectangle and added those areas to find the total area.

I can break apart the rectangle any way I want to, but I like to look for facts that are easy for me to solve. Multiplying by 10 is easy for me. I also could have broken it apart into 8×6 and 8×6. Then I would really only have to solve one fact.

EUREKA MATH   Lesson 10: Apply the distributive property as a strategy to find the total area of a large rectangle by adding two products.   17

©2015 Great Minds. eureka-math.org
G3-M4-HWH-1.3.0-10.2015

G3-M4-Lesson 11

1. The rectangles below have the same area. Move the parentheses to find the unknown side lengths.
    Then, solve.

a.
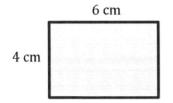

6 cm

4 cm

Area: $4 \times$ __6__ $=$ __24__

Area: __24__ sq cm

I can
multiply
the side
lengths to
find the
area.

b.
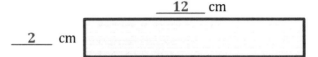

__12__ cm

__2__ cm

Area: $4 \times 6 = (2 \times 2) \times 6$
$\qquad = 2 \times (2 \times 6)$
$\qquad =$ __2__ $\times$ __12__
$\qquad =$ __24__
Area: __24__ sq cm

I can move the parentheses to be
around 2×6. After I multiply 2×6,
I have new side lengths of 2 cm and
12 cm. I can label the side lengths
on the rectangle. The area didn't
change; it's still 24 sq cm.

2. Does Problem 1 show all the possible whole number side lengths for a rectangle with an area of 24
    square centimeters? How do you know?

    *No, Problem 1 doesn't show all possible whole number side lengths. I check by trying to multiply each
    number 1 through 10 by another number to equal 24. If I can find numbers that make 24 when I
    multiply them, then I know those are possible side lengths.*

    *I know $1 \times 24 = 24$. So 1 cm and 24 cm are possible side lengths. I already have a multiplication
    fact for 2, 2×12. I know $3 \times 8 = 24$, which means $8 \times 3 = 24$. I already have a multiplication fact
    for 4, 4×6. That also means that I have a fact for 6, $6 \times 4 = 24$. I know there's not a whole number
    that can be multiplied by 5, 7, 9, or 10 that equals 24. So besides the side lengths from Problem 1,
    other ones could be 1 cm and 24 cm or 8 cm and 3 cm.*

    I know that I can't have side lengths that are both two-digit numbers because
    when I multiply 2 two-digit numbers, the product is much larger than 24.

18   Lesson 11:   Demonstrate the possible whole number side lengths of rectangles with
                            areas of 24, 36, 48, or 72 square units using the associative property.

                                                                            EUREKA
                                                                            MATH™

3.

a. Find the area of the rectangle below.

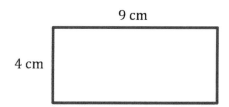

9 cm

4 cm

Area = 4 × 9
= 36
The area of the rectangle is 36 square centimeters.

b. Marcus says a 2 cm by 18 cm rectangle has the same area as the rectangle in part (a). Place parentheses in the equation to find the related fact and solve. Is Marcus correct? Why or why not?

$2 \times 18 = 2 \times (2 \times 9)$
$= (2 \times 2) \times 9$
$= \underline{\quad 4 \quad} \times \underline{\quad 9 \quad}$
$= \underline{\quad 36 \quad}$

Area: $\underline{\quad 36 \quad}$ sq cm

Yes, Marcus is correct because I can rewrite 18 as 2 × 9. Then I can move the parentheses so they are around 2 × 2. After I multiply 2 × 2, I have 4 cm and 9 cm as side lengths, just like in part (a).

$2 \times 18 = 4 \times 9 = 36$

Even though the rectangles in parts (a) and (b) have different side lengths, the areas are the same. Rewriting 18 as 2 × 9 and moving the parentheses helps me to see that 2 × 18 = 4 × 9.

c. Use the expression 4 × 9 to find different side lengths for a rectangle that has the same area as the rectangle in part (a). Show your equations using parentheses. Then, estimate to draw the rectangle and label the side lengths.

$4 \times 9 = 4 \times (3 \times 3)$
$= (4 \times 3) \times 3$
$= 12 \times 3$
$= 36$

Area: 36 sq cm

I can rewrite 9 as 3 × 3. Then I can move the parentheses and multiply to find the new side lengths, 12 cm and 3 cm. I can estimate to draw the new rectangle. If I need to, I can use repeated addition, 12 + 12 + 12, to double check that 12 × 3 = 36.

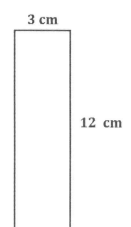

3 cm

12 cm

EUREKA MATH™   Lesson 11:   Demonstrate the possible whole number side lengths of rectangles with
areas of 24, 36, 48, or 72 square units using the associative property.   19

©2015 Great Minds. eureka-math.org
G3-M4-HWH-1.3.0-10.2015

G3-M4-Lesson 12

1. Molly draws a square with sides that are 8 inches long. What is the area of the square?

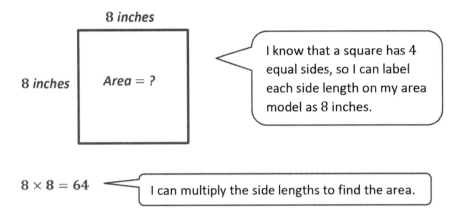

8 inches

8 inches | Area = ?

I know that a square has 4 equal sides, so I can label each side length on my area model as 8 inches.

$8 \times 8 = 64$

I can multiply the side lengths to find the area.

The area of the square is 64 square inches.

2. Each ☐ is 1 square unit. Nathan uses the same square units to draw a 2 × 8 rectangle and says that it has the same area as the rectangle below. Is he correct? Explain why or why not.

4 units

4 units

8 units

2 units

Area = 4 units × 4 units
= 16 square units

Area = 2 units × 8 units
= 16 square units

I can draw an area model with side lengths of 2 units and 8 units to represent Nathan's rectangle. I can multiply the side lengths to find the area.

I can count the units to label the side lengths and then multiply to find the area. Or, I can count all of the units to find the area.

Yes, Nathan is correct. Both rectangles have the same area, 16 square units. The rectangles have different side lengths, but when you multiply the side lengths, you get the same area.

$$4 \times 4 = 2 \times 8 = 16$$

EUREKA MATH

3. A rectangular notepad has a total area of 24 square inches. Draw and label two possible notepads with different side lengths, each having an area of 24 square inches.

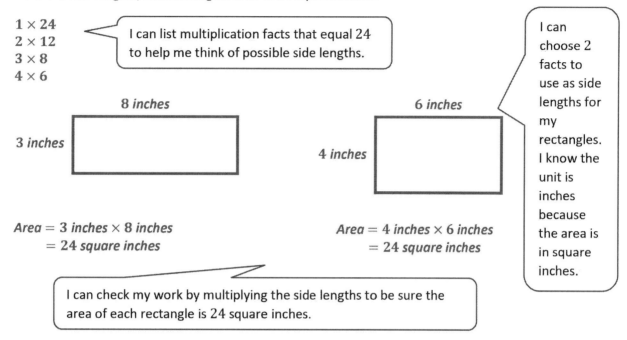

1×24
2×12
3×8
4×6

I can list multiplication facts that equal 24 to help me think of possible side lengths.

I can choose 2 facts to use as side lengths for my rectangles. I know the unit is inches because the area is in square inches.

8 inches

3 inches

6 inches

4 inches

Area = 3 inches × 8 inches
    = 24 square inches

Area = 4 inches × 6 inches
    = 24 square inches

I can check my work by multiplying the side lengths to be sure the area of each rectangle is 24 square inches.

4. Sophia makes the pattern below. Find and explain her pattern. Then, draw the fifth figure in her pattern.

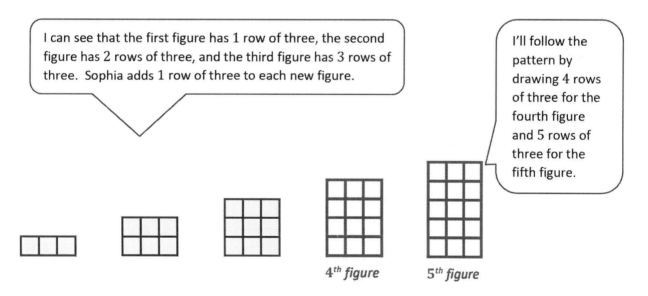

I can see that the first figure has 1 row of three, the second figure has 2 rows of three, and the third figure has 3 rows of three. Sophia adds 1 row of three to each new figure.

I'll follow the pattern by drawing 4 rows of three for the fourth figure and 5 rows of three for the fifth figure.

4ᵗʰ figure

5ᵗʰ figure

Sophia adds 1 row of three to each figure. The fifth figure has 5 rows of three.

G3-M4-Lesson 13

1. The shaded figure below is made up of 2 rectangles. Find the total area of the shaded figure.

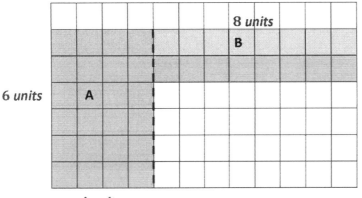

6 units

8 units

B

2 units

A

4 units

> I can count the square units and label the side lengths of each rectangle inside the figure.

$6 \times 4 = 24$ $2 \times 8 = 16$

Area of A: 24 sq units   *Area of B:* 16 sq units

> I can multiply the side lengths to find the area of each rectangle inside the figure.

> I can add the areas of the rectangles to find the total area of the figure.

Area of A+ Area of B= ___24___ sq units + ___16___ sq units = ___40___ sq units

6   10

$24 + 6 = 30$

$30 + 10 = 40$

> I can use a number bond to help me make a ten to add. I can decompose 16 into 6 and 10. $24 + 6 = 30$ and $30 + 10 = 40$. The area of the figure is 40 square units.

Lesson 13:   Find areas by decomposing into rectangles or completing composite figures to form rectangles.

EUREKA MATH

©2015 Great Minds. eureka-math.org
G3-M4-HWH-1.3.0-10.2015

2. The figure shows a small rectangle cut out of a big rectangle. Find the area of the shaded figure.

9 cm

9 cm   5 cm

7 cm

$9 \times 9 = 81$

$5 \times 7 = 35$

> I can multiply the side lengths to find the areas of the large rectangle and the unshaded rectangle.

Area of the shaded figure: ___81___ − ___35___ = ___46___

Area of the shaded figure: ___46___ square centimeters

> I can subtract the area of the unshaded rectangle from the area of the large rectangle. That helps me find just the area of the shaded figure.

3. The figure shows a small rectangle cut out of a big rectangle.

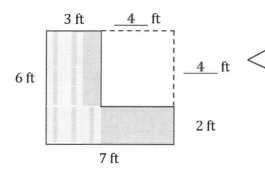

3 ft   __4__ ft

6 ft   __4__ ft

2 ft

7 ft

> I can label this as 4 ft because the opposite side of the rectangle is 6 ft. Since opposite sides of rectangles are equal, I can subtract the known part of this side length, 2 ft, from the opposite side length, 6 ft. 6 ft − 2 ft = 4 ft. I can use a similar strategy to find the other unknown measurement: 7 ft − 3 ft = 4 ft.

a. Label the unknown measurements.

b. Area of the big rectangle: __6__ ft × __7__ ft = __42__ sq ft

c. Area of the small rectangle: __4__ ft × __4__ ft = __16__ sq ft

d. Find the area of just the shaded part.

    $42 \text{ sq ft} - 16 \text{ sq ft} = 26 \text{ sq ft}$

    The area of the shaded figure is 26 sq ft

    > I can subtract the area of the small rectangle from the area of the big rectangle to find the area of just the shaded part.

EUREKA MATH   Lesson 13:   Find areas by decomposing into rectangles or completing composite figures to form rectangles.   23

©2015 Great Minds. eureka-math.org
G3-M4-HWH-1.3.0-10.2015

G3-M4-Lesson 14

1. Find the area of the following figure, which is made up of rectangles.

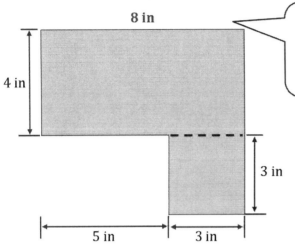

8 in

4 in

3 in

5 in   3 in

I can label this unknown side length as 8 inches because the opposite side is 5 inches and 3 inches, which makes a total of 8 inches. Opposite sides of a rectangle are equal.

$4 \times 8 = 32$

$3 \times 3 = 9$

$32 + 9 = ?$

$31 \quad 1$

$1 + 9 = 10$

$31 + 10 = 41$

I can find the area of the figure by finding the areas of the two rectangles and then adding. I can use a number bond to make adding easier.

The area of the figure is 41 square inches.

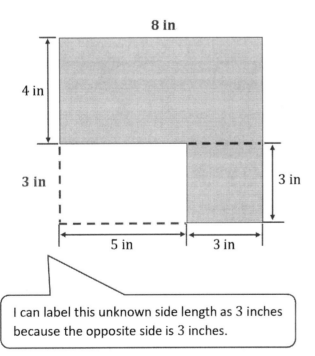

8 in

4 in

3 in   3 in

5 in   3 in

$8 \times 7 = 56$

$3 \times 5 = 15$

$56 - 15 = 41$

Or, I can find the area of the figure by drawing lines to complete the large rectangle. Then I can find the areas of the large rectangle and the unshaded part. I can subtract the area of the unshaded part from the area of the large rectangle. Either way I solve, the area of the figure is 41 square inches.

I can label this unknown side length as 3 inches because the opposite side is 3 inches.

Lesson 14: Find areas by decomposing into rectangles or completing composite figures to form rectangles.

EUREKA MATH

2. The figure below shows a small rectangle cut out of a big rectangle. Find the area of the shaded region.

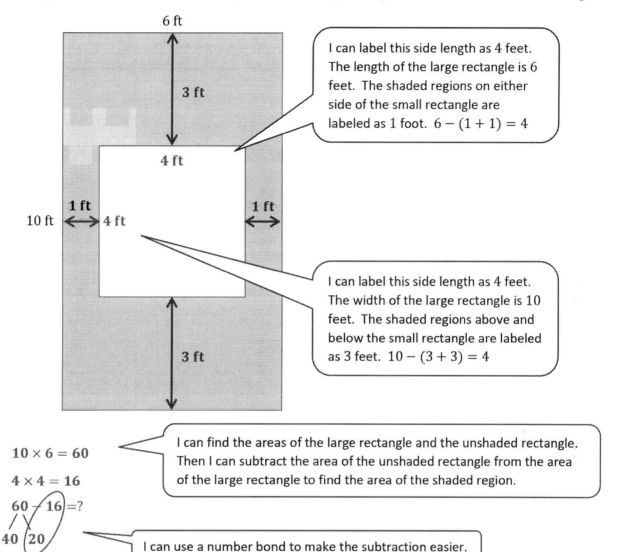

6 ft

3 ft

4 ft

1 ft   1 ft

10 ft 4 ft

3 ft

I can label this side length as 4 feet. The length of the large rectangle is 6 feet. The shaded regions on either side of the small rectangle are labeled as 1 foot. $6 - (1 + 1) = 4$

I can label this side length as 4 feet. The width of the large rectangle is 10 feet. The shaded regions above and below the small rectangle are labeled as 3 feet. $10 - (3 + 3) = 4$

$10 \times 6 = 60$

$4 \times 4 = 16$

$60 - 16 = ?$

40 20

I can find the areas of the large rectangle and the unshaded rectangle. Then I can subtract the area of the unshaded rectangle from the area of the large rectangle to find the area of the shaded region.

I can use a number bond to make the subtraction easier.

$20 - 16 = 4$

$40 + 4 = 44$

The area of the shaded region is 44 square feet.

EUREKA MATH™   Lesson 14:   Find areas by decomposing into rectangles or completing composite figures to form rectangles.   25

©2015 Great Minds. eureka-math.org
G3-M4-HWH-1.3.0-10.2015

G3-M4-Lesson 15

Use a ruler to measure the side lengths of each numbered room in the floor plan in centimeters. Then, find each area. Use the measurements below to match and label the rooms.

Kitchen/Living Room: 78 square centimeters   Bedroom: 48 square centimeters

Bathroom: 24 square centimeters   Hallway: 6 square centimeters

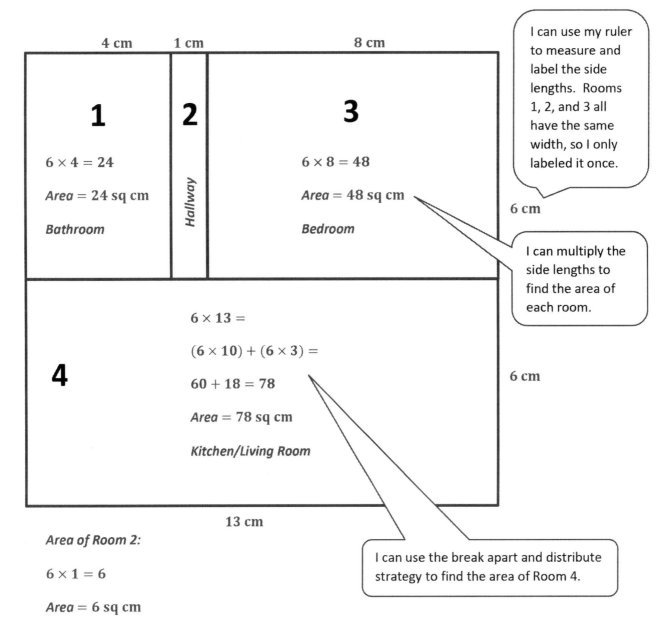

4 cm   1 cm   8 cm

1   **2**   **3**

$6 \times 4 = 24$ $6 \times 8 = 48$

Area = 24 sq cm   *Area = 48 sq cm*

Bathroom   Hallway   *Bedroom*

I can use my ruler to measure and label the side lengths. Rooms 1, 2, and 3 all have the same width, so I only labeled it once.

6 cm

I can multiply the side lengths to find the area of each room.

4

$6 \times 13 =$

$(6 \times 10) + (6 \times 3) =$

$60 + 18 = 78$

Area = 78 sq cm

Kitchen/Living Room

6 cm

13 cm

I can use the break apart and distribute strategy to find the area of Room 4.

Area of Room 2:

$6 \times 1 = 6$

Area = 6 sq cm

26   Lesson 15:   Apply knowledge of area to determine areas of rooms in a given floor
                           plan.

©2015 Great Minds. eureka-math.org
G3-M4-HWH-1.3.0-10.2015

G3-M4-Lesson 16

Mrs. Harris designs her dream classroom on grid paper. The chart shows how much space she gives for each rectangular area. Use the information in the chart to draw and label a possible design for Mrs. Harris's classroom.

Reading area	48 square units	6×8
Carpet area	72 square units	9×8
Student desk area	90 square units	10×9
Science area	56 square units	7×8
Math area	64 square units	8×8

> I can think of multiplication facts that equal each area. Then I can use the multiplication facts as the side lengths of each rectangular area. I can use the grid to help me draw each rectangular area.

9 units   **10 units**

8 units   **Carpet area**   **Student desk area**   9 units

7 units

Science area

8 units   **Reading area**   **Math area**   8 units

8 units

6 units   8 units

Grade 3
Module 5

G3-M5-Lesson 1

1. A beaker is full when the liquid reaches the fill line shown near the top. Estimate the amount of water in the beaker by shading the drawing as indicated.

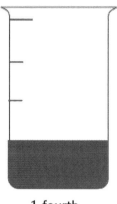

1 fourth

First, I need to partition my whole into 4 equal parts. I can estimate to draw a tick mark halfway between the top and bottom of the beaker and then make tick marks in the middle of each half. After that, I just need to shade 1 of the equal parts.

2. Juanita cut her string cheese into equal pieces as shown below. In the blank below, name the fraction of string cheese represented by the shaded part.

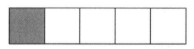

_____1 fifth_____

There are 5 equal parts, so each part is 1 fifth. Only 1 fifth is shaded. I can use unit form to name the fraction since I haven't learned numerical form yet.

3. In the space below, draw a small rectangle. Estimate to split it into 6 equal parts. How many lines did you draw to make 6 equal parts? What is the name of each fractional unit?

It took 5 lines to make 6 equal parts.
Each fractional unit is a sixth!

To split a rectangle into 6 equal parts, I can draw a line to split it in half and then split each half into 3 equal parts. When I have 6 equal parts, my fractional unit is sixths!

EUREKA MATH   Lesson 1:   Specify and partition a whole into equal parts, identifying and   1
                             counting unit fractions using concrete models.

©2015 Great Minds. eureka-math.org
G3-M5-HWH-1.3.0-10.2015

4. Rochelle has a string that is 15 inches long. She cuts it into pieces that are each 5 inches in length. What fraction of the string is 1 piece? Use your strip from the lesson to help you. Draw a picture to show the string and how Rochelle cut it.

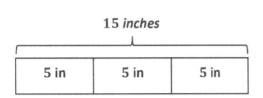

15 *inches*

| 5 in | 5 in | 5 in |

$15 \div 5 = 3$

Each piece is 1 third of the whole string.

This problem reminds me of division because I'm splitting 15 inches into equal parts that are each 5 inches. I can solve $15 \div 5$ to find that Rochelle makes 3 pieces. If there are 3 equal pieces, then each piece is a third!

Lesson 1:   Specify and partition a whole into equal parts, identifying and
                                counting unit fractions using concrete models.

©2015 Great Minds. eureka-math.org
G3-M5-HWH-1.3.0-10.2015

EUREKA MATH™

G3-M5-Lesson 2

1. Circle the strip that is folded to make equal parts.

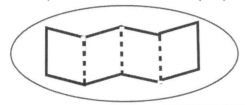 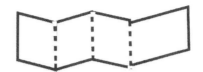

> I can see that all of the parts in the strip on the left are the same size. The strip on the right has some small parts and a bigger part.

2. Dylan plans to eat 1 fourth of his candy bar. His 3 friends want him to share the rest equally. Show how Dylan and his friends can each get an equal share of the candy bar.

Dylan's friends' pieces

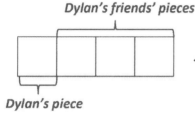

Dylan's piece

> I know that 4 people are sharing the candy bar. I'll draw a fraction strip to represent the candy bar and split it into fourths. I can label Dylan's piece and the pieces that his friends will eat.

3. Nasir baked a pie and cut it into fourths. He then cut each piece in half.
   a. What fraction of the whole pie does each piece represent?

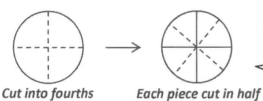

Cut into fourths   *Each piece cut in half*

Each piece represents 1 eighth of the whole pie.

> First, I should draw the pie and split it into 4 equal pieces. Then, I need to cut each part in half. Once I do that, I see that each piece is an eighth!

   b. Nasir ate 1 piece of pie on Tuesday and 2 pieces on Wednesday. What fraction of the whole pie was NOT eaten?

Five eighths of the whole pie was not eaten.

> I can draw the pie and label the pieces Nasir ate. He ate 3 out of the 8 pieces, so 5 are left. So, 5 eighths of Nasir's pie is left!

Lesson 2:   Specify and partition a whole into equal parts, identifying and counting unit fractions by folding fraction strips.

3

©2015 Great Minds. eureka-math.org
G3-M5-HWH-1.3.0-10.2015

G3-M5-Lesson 3

1. Each shape is 1 whole. Estimate to divide each into equal parts. Divide each whole using a different fractional unit. Write the name of the fractional unit on the line below the shape.

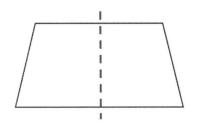   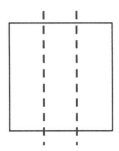   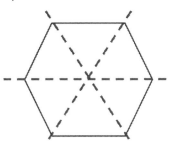

_____ *halves* _____   _____ *thirds* _____   _____ *sixths* _____

> I can pick a different number of equal parts for each shape and split my shapes to match my choices. Then, I'll name the fractional unit. I have to be careful to make sure the parts are equal. My shapes might look different than my friends' because I get to choose the number of equal parts.

2. Anita uses a whole piece of paper to make a chart showing the school days in 1 week. She draws equal-sized boxes to represent each day. Draw a picture to show a possible chart. What fraction of the chart does each day take up?

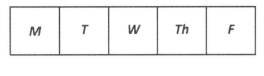

Each day takes up ____ *1 fifth of the chart* ____.

> There are 5 school days in 1 week, so Anita's chart has 5 boxes that are the same size. Each box represents a day and is 1 fifth of the chart.

G3-M5-Lesson 4

1. Each shape is 1 whole. Estimate to equally partition the shape, and shade to show the given fraction.

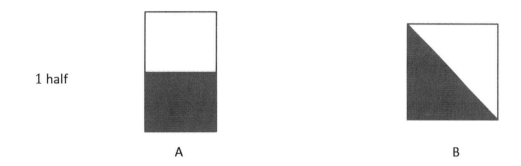

1 half

A

B

> I know that the fraction is 1 half, so I can split each shape into 2 equal parts. Then, I'll shade 1 part in each shape.

2. Each shape represents 1 whole. Match each shape to its fraction.

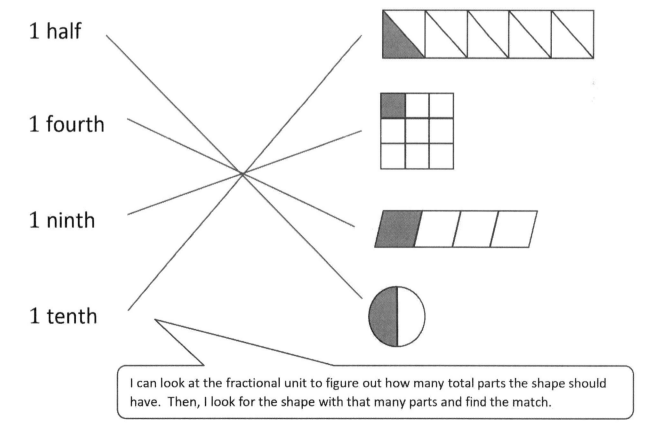

1 half

1 fourth

1 ninth

1 tenth

> I can look at the fractional unit to figure out how many total parts the shape should have. Then, I look for the shape with that many parts and find the match.

EUREKA MATH

Lesson 4: Represent and identify fractional parts of different wholes.

5

©2015 Great Minds. eureka-math.org
G3-M5-HWH-1.3.0-10.2015

G3-M5-Lesson 5

1. Fill in the chart. Then, whisper the fractional unit.

> The fractional unit tells the number of equal parts in the whole. Since there are 6 equal parts, I can whisper, "Sixths."

	Total Number of Equal Parts	Total Number of Equal Parts Shaded	Unit Form	Fraction
	6	1	1 *sixth*	$\frac{1}{6}$

> To write a fraction in unit form, I can write the unit as a word. The answer is 1 sixth because I am counting the number of sixths that are shaded.

> I can write $\frac{1}{6}$ for the fraction because 1 equal part is shaded out of a total of 6 equal parts. I know that $\frac{1}{6}$ is the unit fraction because it names 1 equal part.

Lesson 5:   Partition a whole into equal parts and define the equal parts to identify
              the unit fraction numerically.

EUREKA
MATH™

> If 1 fifth is shaded, then that rectangle must be partitioned into 5 equal parts (fifths). The other rectangle must be partitioned into 8 equal parts (eighths).

2. Draw two identical rectangles. Shade 1 fifth of one rectangle and 1 eighth of the other. Label the unit fractions. Use your rectangles to explain why $\frac{1}{5}$ is greater than $\frac{1}{8}$.

$\frac{1}{5}$

$\frac{1}{8}$

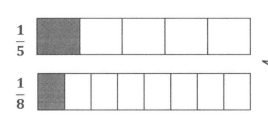

> I can draw two identical rectangles and partition one into fifths and the other into eighths. I can shade 1 equal part in each rectangle to show each unit fraction.

$\frac{1}{5}$ is greater than $\frac{1}{8}$ because both rectangles have 1 equal part shaded, but when the rectangle is cut into 5 equal parts, the parts are bigger than when the rectangle is cut into 8 equal parts.

EUREKA MATH   **Lesson 5:**   Partition a whole into equal parts and define the equal parts to identify the unit fraction numerically.   7

©2015 Great Minds. eureka-math.org
G3-M5-HWH-1.3.0-10.2015

G3-M5-Lesson 6

1. Complete the number sentence. Estimate to partition each strip equally, write the unit fraction inside each unit, and shade the answer.

> 3 fourths is written in unit form. I can complete the number sentence by writing it in fraction form: $\frac{3}{4}$.

> Fourths are the unit, so I'll do my best to draw lines that partition the strip into 4 equal units or parts.

> I can label each equal part with the unit fraction: $\frac{1}{4}$.

$\frac{1}{4}$	$\frac{1}{4}$	$\frac{1}{4}$	$\frac{1}{4}$

3 fourths $= \frac{3}{4}$

> I can shade 3 copies of the unit fraction, $\frac{1}{4}$, to build $\frac{3}{4}$.

2. Mr. Stevens buys 8 liters of soda for a party. His guests drink 1 of the 8 liters of soda.

    a. What fraction of the soda do his guests drink?

$\frac{1}{8}$	$\frac{1}{8}$	$\frac{1}{8}$	$\frac{1}{8}$	$\frac{1}{8}$	$\frac{1}{8}$	$\frac{1}{8}$	$\frac{1}{8}$

drank   left over

His guests drink $\frac{1}{8}$ of the soda.

> I can draw a whole with 8 equal parts because Mr. Stevens buys a total of 8 liters of soda. I can label each part $\frac{1}{8}$ to show that it represents 1 of the 8 liters. Then, I can shade 1 part because the guests drink 1 liter.

    b. What fraction of the soda is left?

$\frac{7}{8}$ of the soda is left.

> I can just count the unshaded units in my diagram and write a sentence to answer the question.

Lesson 6:   Build non-unit fractions less than one whole from unit fractions.   **EUREKA MATH**

©2015 Great Minds. eureka-math.org
G3-M5-HWH-1.3.0-10.2015

G3-M5-Lesson 7

1. Whisper the fraction of the shape that is shaded. Then, match the shape to the amount that is not shaded.

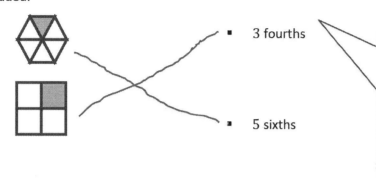

■ 3 fourths

■ 5 sixths

> I can count the total number of parts to find the fractional units, fourths and sixths. Then, I can whisper what part is shaded, "1 sixth" and "1 fourth." I can count how many parts aren't shaded and draw lines to match.

2. Mom lights 10 birthday candles on the cake. Alexis blows out 9 candles. What fraction of the birthday candles are still lit? Draw and explain.

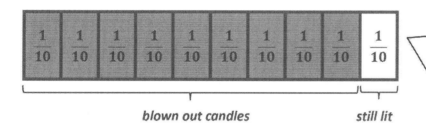

blown out candles   still lit

> I can draw a whole with 10 parts because there is a total of 10 candles on the cake. I can shade the 9 candles that Alexis blows out and count how many are left.

There are a total of 10 candles, but 9 are blown out. That leaves $\frac{1}{10}$ of the candles that are still lit.

> Alexis blew out all but 1 candle. Since there are 10 candles in all, the fraction of candles still lit is $\frac{1}{10}$.

EUREKA
MATH™

Lesson 7:   Identify and represent shaded and non-shaded parts of one whole as fractions.

9

G3-M5-Lesson 8

1. Show a number bond representing what is shaded and unshaded in the figure. Draw a different model that would be represented by the same number bond.

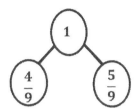

> I can draw a number bond that shows 1 whole broken into 2 parts. One part shows how much of the whole is shaded: $\frac{4}{9}$. The other part shows how much of the whole is unshaded: $\frac{5}{9}$.
>
> Together, $\frac{4}{9}$ and $\frac{5}{9}$ make 1 whole.

> How would I label the number bond if no parts of the whole were shaded? I would still use 1 to label the whole. I could label the shaded parts $\frac{0}{9}$ and the unshaded parts $\frac{9}{9}$. Together, $\frac{0}{9}$ and $\frac{9}{9}$ make 1 whole.

> I can draw this shape to show 1 whole with $\frac{4}{9}$ shaded and $\frac{5}{9}$ unshaded. It can be represented using the same number bond. Lots of other models could work too. Here is one example:

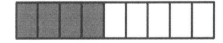

EUREKA
MATH™

This first part is just like Problem 1.

2. Draw a number bond with 2 parts showing the shaded and unshaded fractions of each figure. Decompose both parts of the number bond into unit fractions.

The shaded part of this figure is $\frac{3}{4}$, and the unshaded part is $\frac{1}{4}$.

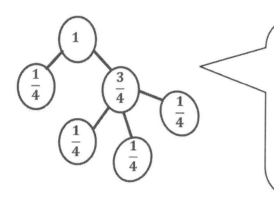

I can draw a number bond with parts of $\frac{1}{4}$ and $\frac{3}{4}$. I know that decomposing is taking apart. $\frac{1}{4}$ is already a unit fraction, but $\frac{3}{4}$ is a non-unit fraction. I can decompose $\frac{3}{4}$ into 3 copies of $\frac{1}{4}$. Now both parts of my number bond are written as unit fractions.

I can check my work by looking at all of the unit fractions. There are 4 copies of $\frac{1}{4}$, which is the same as $\frac{4}{4}$, or 1 whole.

G3-M5-Lesson 9

1. Each shape represents 1 whole. Fill in the chart.

Each of these wholes is partitioned into halves. So, the unit fraction must be $\frac{1}{2}$. Three halves are shaded. I can show that by writing $\frac{3}{2}$.

	Unit Fraction	Total Number of Units Shaded	Fraction Shaded
	$\frac{1}{2}$	3	$\frac{3}{2}$

2. Estimate to draw and shade units on the fraction strips. Solve.

7 fourths = $\frac{7}{4}$

7 fourths is the unit form. I can also write it as $\frac{7}{4}$.

$\frac{1}{4}$	$\frac{1}{4}$	$\frac{1}{4}$	$\frac{1}{4}$

$\frac{1}{4}$	$\frac{1}{4}$	$\frac{1}{4}$	$\frac{1}{4}$

Fourths is the fractional unit. I can partition each whole (fraction strip) into fourths and then label each unit to show that it represents $\frac{1}{4}$. Seven tells me how many units to shade.

Lesson 9: Build and write fractions greater than one whole using unit fractions.

EUREKA MATH

©2015 Great Minds. eureka-math.org
G3-M5-HWH-1.3.0-10.2015

G3-M5-Lesson 10

1. Each fraction strip is 1 whole. The fraction strips are equal in length. Color 1 fractional unit in each strip. Then, answer the questions below.

> I can color one equal part of each whole below.

$\dfrac{1}{8}$

$\dfrac{1}{6}$

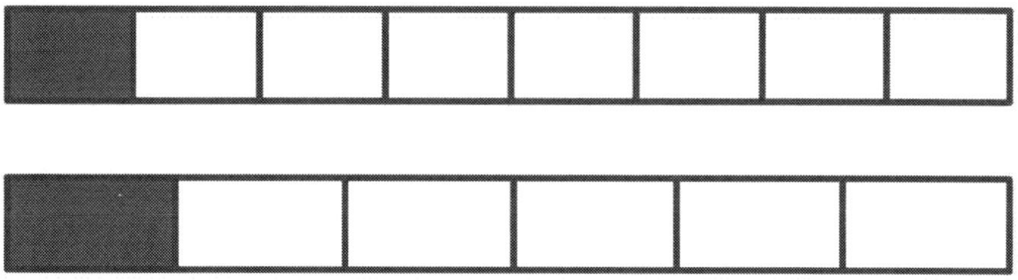

2. Circle *less than* or *greater than*. Whisper the complete sentence.

$\dfrac{1}{8}$ ⟨is less than⟩ / is greater than $\dfrac{1}{6}$

> The fraction strips are equal in length, and they're lined up. I can compare by looking at the fractional units I colored and seeing which one is bigger. $\dfrac{1}{8}$ is smaller than $\dfrac{1}{6}$, so it's less. I could also write that as $\dfrac{1}{8} < \dfrac{1}{6}$ or as 1 eighth < 1 sixth. When I read it, I say, "1 eighth is less than 1 sixth."

> I can draw fraction strips like the ones in Problem 1 to figure out which fraction is bigger.

3. Jerry feeds his dog $\frac{1}{5}$ cup of wet food and $\frac{1}{6}$ cup of dry food for dinner. Does he use more wet food or dry food? Explain your answer using pictures, numbers, and words.

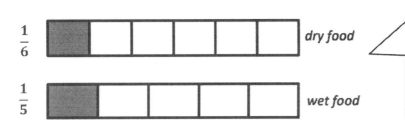

$\frac{1}{6}$ dry food

$\frac{1}{5}$ wet food

> When I draw my fraction strips, they have to be the same size and lined up, or I won't be able to use them to accurately compare the fractions.

Jerry uses more wet food because $\frac{1}{5}$ is greater than $\frac{1}{6}$. When you cut a whole into more pieces, the pieces get smaller.

4. Use >, <, or = to compare.

a. 1 half $\left(>\right)$ $\frac{1}{8}$

b. 1 fifth $\left(<\right)$ 1 third

> I can draw a picture to help me compare the fractions, or I can think about the size of the fractional units. I know that the more equal parts there are, the smaller each part is. That means that halves are bigger than eighths and fifths are smaller than thirds.

©2015 Great Minds. eureka-math.org
G3-M5-HWH-1.3.0-10.2015

G3-M5-Lesson 11

1. Label the unit fraction. In each blank, draw and label the same whole with a shaded unit fraction that makes the sentence true. There might be more than 1 correct way to make the sentence true.

> I need to draw the same rectangle and partition it into equal parts that are greater than $\frac{1}{3}$ because the sentence reads "$\frac{1}{3}$ is less than ___."

> This shape is partitioned into thirds, so $\frac{1}{3}$ is the unit fraction.

$\frac{1}{3}$ is less than $\frac{1}{2}$

> Halves are greater than thirds, so I can draw a rectangle and partition it into halves. I can shade 1 part and label the shaded part as $\frac{1}{2}$. Now my sentence says "$\frac{1}{3}$ is less than $\frac{1}{2}$." That's true.

2. Luna drinks $\frac{1}{5}$ of a large water bottle. Gabriel drinks $\frac{1}{3}$ of a small water bottle. Gabriel says, "I drank more than you because $\frac{1}{3} > \frac{1}{5}$."

    a. Use pictures and words to explain Gabriel's mistake.

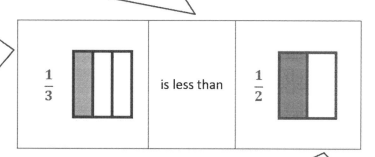

$\frac{1}{3}$ $\frac{1}{5}$

Gabriel can't compare how much water he and Luna drank. Since the wholes are different, $\frac{1}{5}$ might be bigger than $\frac{1}{3}$ like in the picture I drew.

> The important thing I notice is that the water bottles are different sizes. That means the wholes are different, so I can't compare the fractions.

b. How could you change the problem so that Gabriel is correct? Use pictures and words to explain.

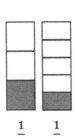

$\frac{1}{3}$ $\frac{1}{5}$

> I can draw models for Gabriel and Luna that are the same size. I can partition and shade the models to show $\frac{1}{3}$ and $\frac{1}{5}$. It's easy to compare the fractions now that the wholes are the same.

I could change the problem to make the wholes the same size. I could say that they both drank water from the same-sized water bottles. Then $\frac{1}{3}$ is greater than $\frac{1}{5}$. When the whole is the same, fifths are smaller than thirds.

Lesson 11: Compare unit fractions with different-sized models representing the whole.

©2015 Great Minds. eureka-math.org
G3-M5-HWH-1.3.0-10.2015

EUREKA MATH

G3-M5-Lesson 12

1. Each shape represents the given unit fraction. Estimate to draw a possible whole. Draw a number bond that matches.

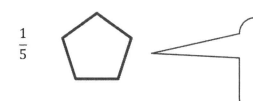

$\frac{1}{5}$

> The 5 in the fraction tells me that the unit is fifths, so there are 5 equal parts in the whole. Since this shape is a unit fraction, I can draw 5 copies of it to build my whole. There are lots of different shapes I could draw.

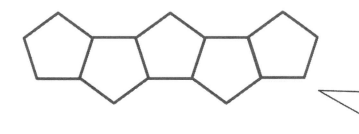

> I can make 5 copies of the unit fraction to make a whole. It's important that there are no gaps or overlaps. Overlaps would mean the parts aren't equal. If there were gaps, the whole might not be clear.

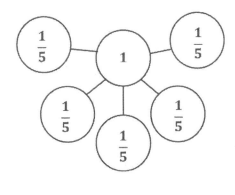

> I can draw a number bond that shows the part–whole relationship between the unit fractions and the whole. This matches the drawing because it shows that 5 copies of $\frac{1}{5}$ make a whole, or 1.

2. Cathy and Laura use this shape to represent the unit fraction $\frac{1}{4}$. They each use it to draw the wholes below. James says they both did it correctly. Do you agree with him? Explain your answer.

Cathy's Shape   Laura's Shape

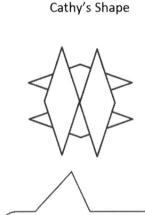   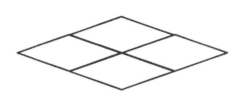

It looks like Cathy drew 4 copies of the shape, but since they're overlapping, it's really hard to tell whether or not the parts are equal sizes.

I can easily see in Laura's shape that she drew 4 copies of the shape to make a whole.

No, I don't agree with James. Cathy's shape has a lot of overlapping, which makes it really hard to see what the whole is. The overlapping also makes it difficult for me to see how many parts make up the whole and whether or not the parts are equal.

©2015 Great Minds. eureka-math.org
G3-M5-HWH-1.3.0-10.2015

G3-M5-Lesson 13

1.

The shape represents 1 whole. Write a unit fraction to describe the shaded part.	The shaded part represents 1 whole. Divide 1 whole to show the same unit fraction you wrote in part (a).
a. 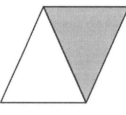 $\frac{1}{2}$	b. 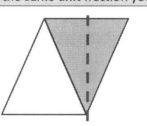

Both triangles make up the whole. Since there are 2 equal parts, that means that the fractional unit is halves and the unit fraction is $\frac{1}{2}$. I can write $\frac{1}{2}$ to represent the shaded part.

This time just the shaded part represents the whole. I have to think about how I can partition just the shaded part into halves since the unit fraction in part (a) is $\frac{1}{2}$. Since halves means 2 equal parts, I can draw a dotted line to partition the shaded whole into 2 equal parts.

2.

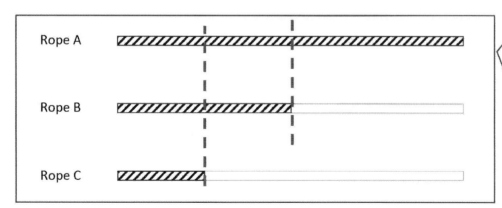

I can draw a dotted line to help me compare the lengths of Ropes A and B. It looks like Rope B is about $\frac{1}{2}$ the length of Rope A. Half of 10 feet is 5 feet.

a. If Rope A measures 10 feet long, then Rope B is about __5__ feet long.

EUREKA MATH

Lesson 13: Identify a shaded fractional part in different ways depending on the designation of the whole.

19

©2015 Great Minds. eureka-math.org
G3-M5-HWH-1.3.0-10.2015

b. About how many copies of Rope C equal the length of Rope A? Draw a number bond to help you.

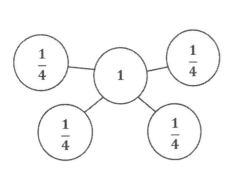

I can draw another dotted line to help me compare the lengths of Ropes C and A. That shows me that Rope C is about $\frac{1}{4}$ the length of Rope A.

The whole in my number bond, 1, represents the length of Rope A. The 4 parts are the number of copies of Rope C it would take to equal the length of Rope A.

About 4 copies of Rope C equal the length of Rope A.

Lesson 13:   Identify a shaded fractional part in different ways depending on the designation of the whole.

©2015 Great Minds. eureka-math.org
G3-M5-HWH-1.3.0-10.2015

G3-M5-Lesson 14

1. Draw a number bond for each fractional unit. Partition the fraction strip to show the unit fractions of the number bond. Use the fraction strip to help you label the fractions on the number line. Be sure to label the fractions at 0 and 1.

Thirds

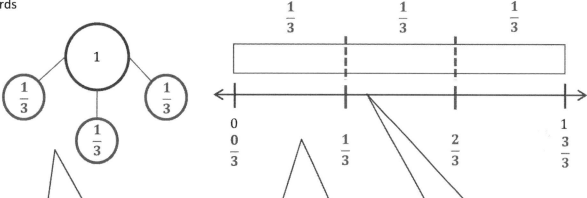

The fractional unit is thirds. The number bond shows that three copies of $\frac{1}{3}$ make 1 whole.

I partitioned the fraction strip (the rectangle above the number line) into 3 equal parts and labeled each part $\frac{1}{3}$. The 3 copies of $\frac{1}{3}$ on my fraction strip match the 3 copies of $\frac{1}{3}$ shown by my number bond.

My number line and fraction strip are the same length, so I used the partitions on my fraction strip to help me know where to make tick marks on my number line. Then, I counted thirds from left to right and labeled how many thirds I counted at each tick mark: $\frac{0}{3}, \frac{1}{3}, \frac{2}{3}, \frac{3}{3}$.

2. A rope is 1 meter long. Mr. Lee makes a knot every $\frac{1}{4}$ meter. The first knot is at $\frac{1}{4}$ meter. The last knot is at 1 meter. Draw and label a number line from 0 meters to 1 meter to show where Mr. Lee makes knots. Label all the fractions, including 0 fourths and 4 fourths. Label 0 meters and 1 meter, too.

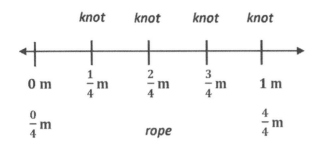

> Mr. Lee makes knots every $\frac{1}{4}$ meter, so his rope must be partitioned into 4 equal parts.

> I can draw a number line to represent Mr. Lee's rope and then partition it into 4 equal parts. I can count by fourths from left to right starting at 0, or 0 fourths, and label them at each tick mark: 0 fourths, 1 fourth, 2 fourths, 3 fourths, 4 fourths, or 1 meter.

Lesson 14:   Place fractions on a number line with endpoints 0 and 1.

EUREKA MATH

G3-M5-Lesson 15

1. Estimate to label the given fraction on the number line. Be sure to label the fractions at 0 and 1. Write the fractions above the number line. Draw a number bond to match your number line.

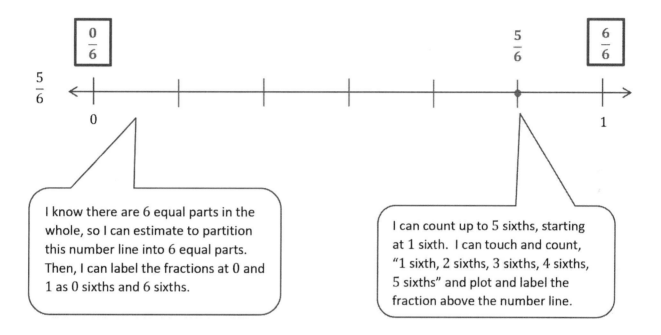

$\frac{0}{6}$ $\frac{5}{6}$ $\frac{6}{6}$

$\frac{5}{6}$

0   1

I know there are 6 equal parts in the whole, so I can estimate to partition this number line into 6 equal parts. Then, I can label the fractions at 0 and 1 as 0 sixths and 6 sixths.

I can count up to 5 sixths, starting at 1 sixth. I can touch and count, "1 sixth, 2 sixths, 3 sixths, 4 sixths, 5 sixths" and plot and label the fraction above the number line.

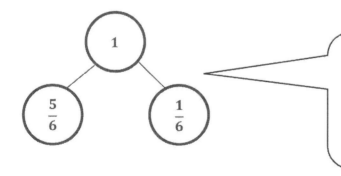

I can draw a 2-part number bond of 1 whole with 1 part labeled 5 sixths and the other part labeled 1 sixth. This number bond shows the fraction I plotted and the other part of the number line.

2. Claire made 6 equally spaced knots on her ribbon as shown.

$$\frac{0}{5} \qquad \frac{1}{5} \qquad \frac{2}{5} \qquad \frac{3}{5} \qquad \frac{4}{5} \qquad \frac{5}{5}$$

> I know that I need to count the number of equal parts, not the number of knots Claire made. Even though Claire made 6 knots, there are 5 equal parts.

a. Starting at the first knot and ending at the last knot, how many equal parts are formed by the 6 knots? Label each fraction at the knot.

There are 5 equal parts.

> Since there are 5 equal parts, I can label the fractions as fifths, starting with 0 fifths at the first knot and 5 fifths at the last knot.

b. What fraction of the rope is labeled at the fourth knot?

$$\frac{3}{5}$$

> I know that the first knot is 0 fifths. When I touch and count by fifths to the fourth knot, I count 3 fifths.

24   Lesson 15:   Place any fraction on a number line with endpoints 0 and 1.

©2015 Great Minds. eureka-math.org
G3-M5-HWH-1.3.0-10.2015

EUREKA
MATH

G3-M5-Lesson 16

1. Estimate to equally partition and label the fractions on the number line. Label the whole numbers as fractions, and box them.

fourths

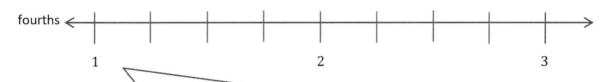

In earlier practice, the left endpoint on the number line was 0. Here it starts at 1. The arrows on the number line tell me that there are more numbers, but it just doesn't show them. I can still partition the number line into fourths.

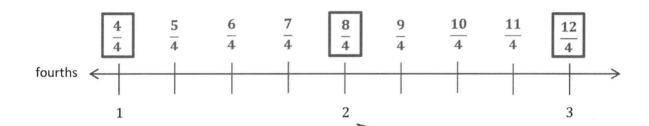

fourths

I know there are 4 fourths in 1, so I can label 4 fourths above the 1. Then, I can count on by fourths and label the fractions up to 3.

I see that 8 fourths is at the same point as 2. That means 8 fourths and 2 are equivalent. It's the same with 12 fourths and 3. I can box these numbers to show the whole numbers as fractions.

EUREKA
MATH™

Lesson 16:   Place whole number fractions and fractions between whole numbers on
               the number line.

25

©2015 Great Minds. eureka-math.org
G3-M5-HWH-1.3.0-10.2015

2. Draw a number line with endpoints 4 and 6. Label the whole numbers. Estimate to partition each interval into sixths, and label them. Box the fractions that are located at the same points as whole numbers.

I can first draw a number line with the endpoints 4 and 6. I see that 5 is missing from the number line, so I need to mark and label 5 at the point halfway between 4 and 6. After labeling the whole numbers, I can partition each interval into 6 equal lengths.

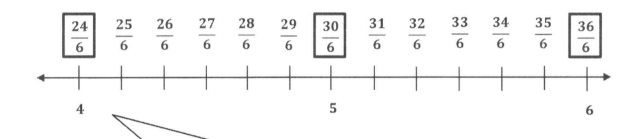

This number line starts at 4. I need to figure out how many sixths are equivalent to 4. I know 6 copies of 1 sixth make 1, so 12 copies of 1 sixth make 2, 18 copies make 3, and 24 copies make 4. I notice a pattern. I am skip-counting by 6 sixths to get to the next whole number. That means I can also just multiply 4 × 6 sixths to get 24 sixths. Now that I know 24 sixths is equivalent to 4, I can count on to fill in the rest of my number line.

Lesson 16: Place whole number fractions and fractions between whole numbers on the number line.

EUREKA MATH™

G3-M5-Lesson 17

> I notice that all of these fractions are thirds. That means I need to partition my number line into thirds.

1. Locate and label the following fractions on the number line.

$$\frac{16}{3} \qquad \frac{20}{3} \qquad \frac{12}{3} \qquad \frac{14}{3} \qquad \frac{10}{3}$$

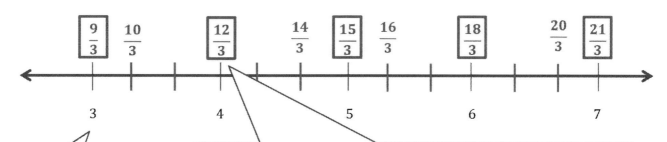

> The number line begins with 3 because all of the given fractions are greater than 3.

> The fractions I have to find and label are out of order. To help me place them on the number line I can first label the whole numbers as thirds. I'll box them so it's easy to remember they represent whole numbers. I can count by threes to find each number of thirds: 1 = 3 thirds, 2 = 6 thirds, 3 = 9 thirds, 4 = 12 thirds, 5 = 15 thirds, 6 = 18 thirds, 7 = 21 thirds. Now it's easier to label all of the given fractions on the number line.

©2015 Great Minds. eureka-math.org
G3-M5-HWH-1.3.0-10.2015

2. Students measure the lengths of their earthworms in science class. Nathan's measures 3 inches long. Elisha's is $\frac{15}{4}$ inches long. Whose earthworm is longer? Draw a number line to help prove your answer.

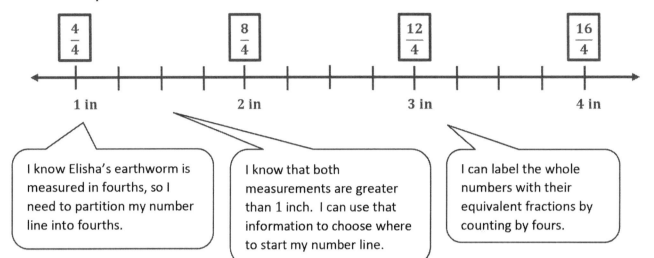

I know Elisha's earthworm is measured in fourths, so I need to partition my number line into fourths.

I know that both measurements are greater than 1 inch. I can use that information to choose where to start my number line.

I can label the whole numbers with their equivalent fractions by counting by fours.

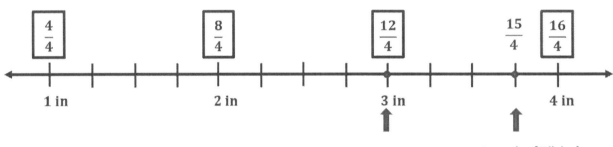

Length of Nathan's earthworm

Length of Elisha's earthworm

Now I can plot and label Nathan's and Elisha's measurements on the number line to compare whose earthworm is longer.

Elisha's earthworm is longer. I can see that 3 inches, or $\frac{12}{4}$, comes before $\frac{15}{4}$ inches on the number line.

EUREKA MATH

©2015 Great Minds. eureka-math.org
G3-M5-HWH-1.3.0-10.2015

G3-M5-Lesson 18

Place the two fractions on the number line. Circle the fraction with the distance closest to 0. Then, compare using $>$, $<$, or $=$.

$$\frac{0}{3} \quad \left(\frac{1}{3}\right) \quad \frac{2}{3} \quad \frac{3}{3}$$

1. $\quad \frac{2}{3} \left(>\right) \frac{1}{3}$

Both fractions are thirds, so I need to partition my number line into thirds. Then, I can count and label the 2 fractions on the number line and circle the fraction with the distance closest to 0.

I can think of the number line like a giant ruler. When I use a ruler, I start at 0 to measure. Then, I can compare the measurements. It's the same when comparing fractions. The fraction's distance from 0 helps me to compare. 1 third is a shorter distance from 0, so it is the smaller fraction. 2 thirds is a greater distance away from 0, so it is the larger fraction.

$$\frac{0}{2} \quad \frac{1}{2} \quad \frac{2}{2}$$

2. $\quad \frac{1}{2} \left(=\right) \frac{2}{4}$

$$\frac{0}{4} \quad \frac{1}{4} \quad \frac{2}{4} \quad \frac{3}{4} \quad \frac{4}{4}$$

These fractions have different numbers on the bottom. I'll count and label halves above my number line and fourths below.

I know these are equivalent fractions because they are the same distance from 0 on the number line. I plotted them at the same point.

3. To get to the library, John walks $\frac{1}{3}$ mile from his house. Susan walks $\frac{3}{4}$ mile from her house. Draw a number line to model how far each student walks. Who walks farther? Explain how you know using pictures, numbers, and words.

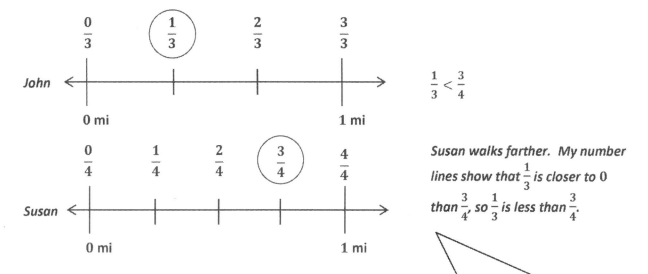

$\frac{1}{3} < \frac{3}{4}$

Susan walks farther. My number lines show that $\frac{1}{3}$ is closer to 0 than $\frac{3}{4}$, so $\frac{1}{3}$ is less than $\frac{3}{4}$.

I can draw 2 number lines. John's number line is partitioned into thirds, and Susan's number line is partitioned into fourths. I have to make sure that both my number lines have the same distance from 0 to 1 because if the whole changes, then the distance between the fractions also changes. I wouldn't be able to compare the 2 distances accurately.

Lesson 18:   Compare fractions and whole numbers on the number line by reasoning about their distance from 0.   **EUREKA MATH**

©2015 Great Minds. eureka-math.org
G3-M5-HWH-1.3.0-10.2015

G3-M5-Lesson 19

1. Divide the number line into the given fractional unit. Then, label the fractions. Write each whole number as a fraction using the given unit.

   Fifths

   $\frac{3}{5}$ $\frac{14}{5}$ $\frac{8}{5}$

   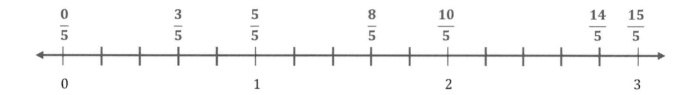

2. Use the number line above to compare the following using $>$, $<$, or $=$.

   I can compare these numbers by looking at their distance from 0. I know that the smaller number will be to the left of the larger number because that's closer to 0.

   $\frac{3}{5}$ $<$ $\frac{8}{5}$ $\frac{7}{5}$ $<$ 2   3 $>$ $\frac{14}{5}$

   3 fifths is a shorter distance from 0, so it is a smaller fraction. 8 fifths is a greater distance from 0, so it is a larger fraction.

   Writing each whole number as a fraction on the number line helps me compare whole numbers and fractions.

EUREKA
MATH™   Lesson 19:   Understand distance and position on the number line as strategies for   31
                            comparing fractions. (Optional)

©2015 Great Minds. eureka-math.org
G3-M5-HWH-1.3.0-10.2015

3. Use the number line from Problem 1 to help you. Which is larger: 2 or $\frac{9}{5}$? Use words, pictures, and
    numbers to explain your answer.

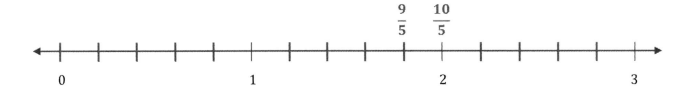

2 is larger than $\frac{9}{5}$. We can see that $\frac{9}{5}$ is to the left of 2 on the number line, which means that $\frac{9}{5}$ is closer
to 0, so $\frac{9}{5}$ is less than 2.

Lesson 19:   Understand distance and position on the number line as strategies for
                                comparing fractions. (Optional)

©2015 Great Minds. eureka-math.org
G3-M5-HWH-1.3.0-10.2015

G3-M5-Lesson 20

1. These two shapes both show $\frac{3}{4}$ shaded.

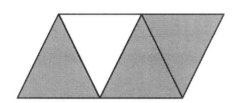   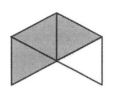

> I can see that both shapes are made up of triangles, but the size of the triangles is different in each shape.

a. Are the shaded areas equivalent? Why or why not?

No, the shaded areas are not equivalent. Both shapes have 3 shaded triangles, but the size of the triangles in each shape is different. That means that the shaded areas can't be equivalent.

b. Draw two different representations of $\frac{3}{4}$ that are equivalent.

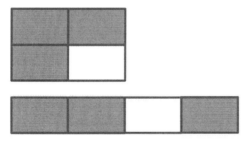

> I can use the same units to draw two different representations of $\frac{3}{4}$ that are equivalent. I can rearrange the units to make a different shape.

2. Brian walked $\frac{2}{4}$ mile down the street. Wilson walked $\frac{2}{4}$ mile around the block. Who walked more? Explain your thinking.

Brian _____

Wilson ☐

> I can see that these shapes are different, but I need to think about the units. They both walked $\frac{2}{4}$ mile, and since the units (miles) and the fractions are the same, the fractions are equivalent.

They both walked the same amount because the units are the same. They both walked $\frac{2}{4}$ mile even though they walked in different ways. Brian walked in a straight line, and Wilson walked in a rectangular shape. The shapes look different, but they are both the same distance, $\frac{2}{4}$ mile.

G3-M5-Lesson 21

1. Use the fractional units on the left to count up on the number line. Label the missing fractions on the blanks.

> I can count by halves to help me label the number line. 0 halves, 1 half, 2 halves, 3 halves, 4 halves. I can do the same thing with eighths.

halves

$\frac{0}{2}$ $\boxed{\frac{1}{2}}$ $\frac{2}{2}$ $\triangle \frac{3}{2}$ $\frac{4}{2}$ ★

eighths

0 $\frac{1}{8}$ $\frac{2}{8}$ $\frac{3}{8}$ $\boxed{\frac{4}{8}}$ $\frac{5}{8}$ $\frac{6}{8}$ $\frac{7}{8}$ 1 $\frac{9}{8}$ $\frac{10}{8}$ $\frac{11}{8}$ $\frac{12}{8}$ $\frac{13}{8}$ $\frac{14}{8}$ $\frac{15}{8}$ 2

$\frac{0}{8}$ $\frac{8}{8}$ $\frac{16}{8}$ ★

2. Use the number line above to do the following:

-   Circle fractions equal to 1.
-   Draw a box around fractions equal to 1 half.
-   Draw a star next to fractions equal to 2.
-   Draw a triangle around fractions equal to 3 halves.
-   Write a pair of fractions that are equivalent.

> I know that equivalent fractions are at the same point on the number line. I can see that $\frac{2}{2}$ and $\frac{8}{8}$ are equal to 1 because they are at the same point on the number line.

$$\underline{\quad \frac{3}{2} \quad} = \underline{\quad \frac{12}{8} \quad}$$

> $\frac{3}{2}$ and $\frac{12}{8}$ are equivalent fractions because they are at the same point on the number line.

Lesson 21:   Recognize and show that equivalent fractions refer to the same point on the number line.

EUREKA MATH

G3-M5-Lesson 22

1. Write the shaded fraction of each figure on the blank. Then, draw a line to match the equivalent fractions.

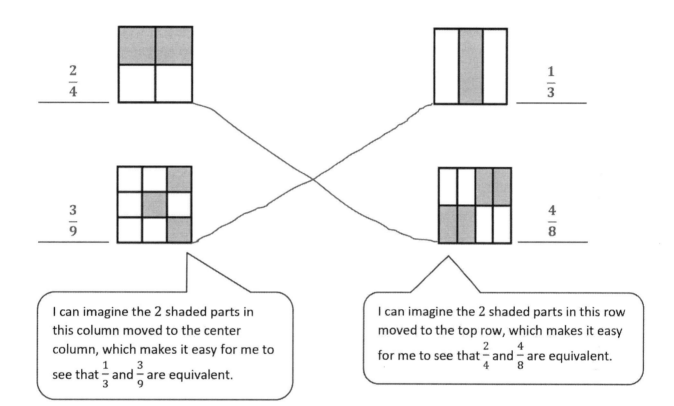

$\frac{2}{4}$ _____

$\frac{1}{3}$ _____

$\frac{3}{9}$ _____

$\frac{4}{8}$ _____

I can imagine the 2 shaded parts in this column moved to the center column, which makes it easy for me to see that $\frac{1}{3}$ and $\frac{3}{9}$ are equivalent.

I can imagine the 2 shaded parts in this row moved to the top row, which makes it easy for me to see that $\frac{2}{4}$ and $\frac{4}{8}$ are equivalent.

2. Complete the fraction to make a true statement.

$$\frac{3}{6} = \frac{6}{12}$$

I can count the shaded parts in the second shape to see that $\frac{3}{6}$ and $\frac{6}{12}$ are equivalent.

EUREKA
MATH™

Lesson 22:   Generate simple equivalent fractions by using visual fraction models and the
             number line.

35

©2015 Great Minds. eureka-math.org
G3-M5-HWH-1.3.0-10.2015

3. Why does it take 2 copies of $\frac{1}{4}$ to show the same amount as 1 copy of $\frac{1}{2}$? Explain your answer in words and pictures.

$\frac{1}{2}$

$\frac{2}{4}$

> I can draw 2 models, where each whole is the same size. Then, I can partition and shade to show that $\frac{2}{4} = \frac{1}{2}$.

There is double the number of equal parts in fourths than halves, so you need double the number of copies to show equivalent fractions.

4. How many eighths does it take to make the same amount as $\frac{1}{4}$? Explain your answer in words and pictures.

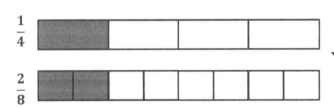

$\frac{1}{4}$

$\frac{2}{8}$

> My models show that for every $\frac{1}{4}$, there are $\frac{2}{8}$. Eighths are smaller units than fourths, so it takes more eighths to equal $\frac{1}{4}$.

It takes 2 eighths to make the same amount as $\frac{1}{4}$ because there is double the number of equal parts in eighths, so it takes double the number of copies.

5. A pizza was cut into 6 equal slices. If Lizzie ate $\frac{1}{3}$ of the pizza, how many slices did she eat? Explain your answer using a number line and words.

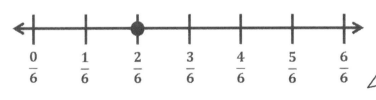

$\frac{0}{6}$ $\frac{1}{6}$ $\frac{2}{6}$ $\frac{3}{6}$ $\frac{4}{6}$ $\frac{5}{6}$ $\frac{6}{6}$

$\frac{0}{3}$ $\frac{1}{3}$ $\frac{2}{3}$ $\frac{3}{3}$

> I can draw two number lines that are the same size. I can partition one into sixths and the other into thirds. My number lines show that $\frac{1}{3}$ is equivalent to $\frac{2}{6}$. I also could have drawn one number line and partition it into thirds and sixths.

Lizzie ate 2 slices of pizza because my number lines show that $\frac{1}{3} = \frac{2}{6}$, and $\frac{2}{6}$ means that she ate 2 of the 6 pieces.

Lesson 22: Generate simple equivalent fractions by using visual fraction models and the number line.

EUREKA MATH™

G3-M5-Lesson 23

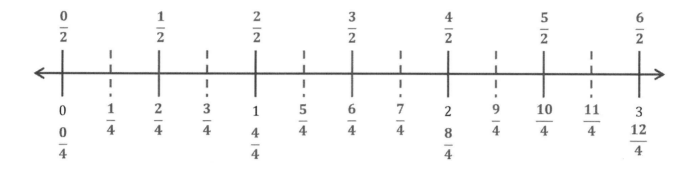

1. On the number line above, divide each whole into halves, and label the halves above the line.

2. On the number line above, divide each whole into fourths, and label the fourths below the line.

3. Write the fractions that name the same place on the number line.

$\frac{0}{4} = \frac{0}{2}$ $\frac{2}{4} = \frac{1}{2}$ $\frac{4}{4} = \frac{2}{2}$ $\frac{6}{4} = \frac{3}{2}$

$\frac{8}{4} = \frac{4}{2}$ $\frac{10}{4} = \frac{5}{2}$ $\frac{12}{4} = \frac{6}{2}$

> I can use an equal sign to show that these are equivalent because they are at the same point on the number line.

4. Use your number line to help you name the fractions equivalent to $\frac{14}{4}$ and $\frac{8}{2}$. Draw the part of the number line that would include these fractions below, and label it.

$\frac{14}{4} = \frac{7}{2}$ $\frac{8}{2} = \frac{16}{4}$

> I know these fractions are equivalent because they are at the same point on the number line.

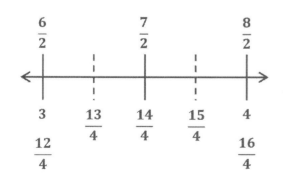

> I can use my number line to count on by halves to $\frac{8}{2}$, which is the same as 4. I can draw a number line showing the interval of 3 to 4 and partition and label the halves and fourths.

EUREKA
MATH™

Lesson 23:   Generate simple equivalent fractions by using visual fraction models and the   37
             number line.

©2015 Great Minds. eureka-math.org
G3-M5-HWH-1.3.0-10.2015

5. Write two different fraction names for the dot on the number line. You may use halves, fourths, or eighths.

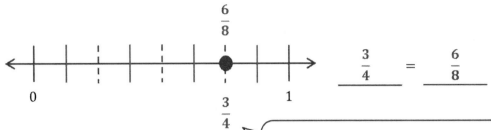

$$\frac{3}{4} = \frac{6}{8}$$

> I can partition the interval into eighths. Then, I can count by fourths and eighths to label the dot on the number line.

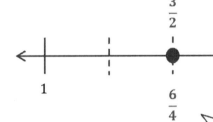

$$\frac{6}{4} = \frac{3}{2}$$

> I can count by halves and fourths to label the dot on the number line. I can start counting at $\frac{2}{2}$ and $\frac{4}{4}$ because the interval starts at 1, not 0.

6. Megan and Hunter bake two equal-sized pans of brownies. Megan cuts her pan of brownies into fourths, and Hunter cuts his pan of brownies into eighths. Megan eats $\frac{1}{4}$ of her pan of brownies. If Hunter wants to eat the same amount of brownies as Megan, how many of his brownies will he have to eat? Write the answer as a fraction. Draw a number line to explain your answer.

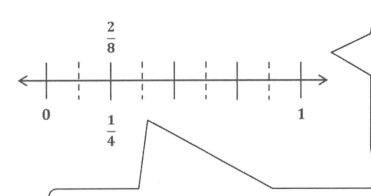

> I can draw a number line and partition it into fourths and eighths. I can count by fourths to find and label the point $\frac{1}{4}$. I can count by eighths to find and label the point that is equivalent to $\frac{1}{4}$.

The fractions $\frac{1}{4}$ and $\frac{2}{8}$ are at the same point on the number line, so they are equivalent.

Hunter needs to eat $\frac{2}{8}$ of his brownies to eat the same amount as Megan because $\frac{2}{8} = \frac{1}{4}$.

Lesson 23: Generate simple equivalent fractions by using visual fraction models and the number line.

EUREKA MATH™

©2015 Great Minds. eureka-math.org
G3-M5-HWH-1.3.0-10.2015

G3-M5-Lesson 24

1. Complete the number bond as indicated by the fractional unit. Partition the number line into the given fractional unit, and label the fractions. Rename 0 and 1 as fractions of the given unit.

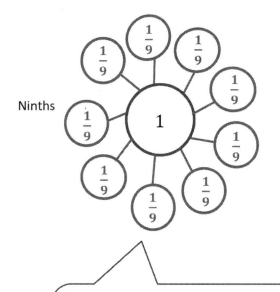

Ninths

$$\frac{0}{9} \quad \frac{1}{9} \quad \frac{2}{9} \quad \frac{3}{9} \quad \frac{4}{9} \quad \frac{5}{9} \quad \frac{6}{9} \quad \frac{7}{9} \quad \frac{8}{9} \quad \frac{9}{9}$$

0   1

> I can partition the number line into nine equal parts and count by ninths to label the fractions.

> The fractional unit, ninths, tells me that I need to make nine parts on my number bond. Each part is $\frac{1}{9}$ because 9 copies of $\frac{1}{9}$ make a whole.

2. Mrs. Smith bakes two large apple pies. She cuts one pie into fourths and gives it to her daughter. She cuts the other pie into eighths and gives it to her son. Her son says, "My pie is bigger because it has more pieces than yours!" Is he correct? Use words, pictures, or a number line to help you explain.

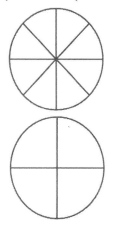

son's pie: eighths

daughter's pie: fourths

No, he is not correct. His pie has more pieces, but the pieces are smaller than his sister's pieces. Both pies are the same size so they both have the same amount of pie, even though they have a different number of pieces.

> I can draw two same-sized circles to represent the pies. I can partition the circles into eighths and fourths.

EUREKA
MATH™   Lesson 24:   Express whole numbers as fractions and recognize equivalence with different   39
                              units.

                ©2015 Great Minds. eureka-math.org
                G3-M5-HWH-1.3.0-10.2015

G3-M5-Lesson 25

1. Label the following models as fractions inside the boxes.

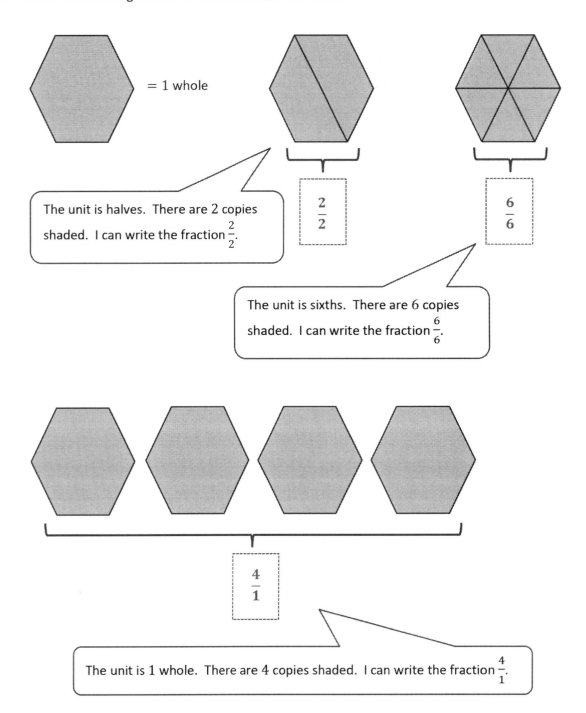

$$= 1 \text{ whole}$$

The unit is halves. There are 2 copies shaded. I can write the fraction $\frac{2}{2}$.

$$\frac{2}{2}$$

$$\frac{6}{6}$$

The unit is sixths. There are 6 copies shaded. I can write the fraction $\frac{6}{6}$.

$$\frac{4}{1}$$

The unit is 1 whole. There are 4 copies shaded. I can write the fraction $\frac{4}{1}$.

Lesson 25: Express whole number fractions on the number line when the unit interval is 1.

EUREKA
MATH™

2. Fill in the missing whole numbers in the boxes below the number line. Use the pattern to rename the whole numbers as fractions in the boxes above the number line.

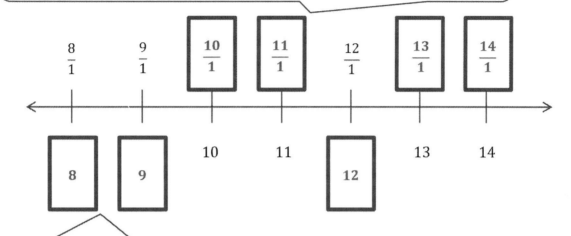

> I see a pattern in how whole numbers are written as fractions. I can use the whole numbers on the bottom to help me fill in the fractions on the top. $10 = \frac{10}{1}$

> I can use the fractions on the top to help me fill in the whole numbers on the bottom. $\frac{8}{1} = 8$

3. Explain the difference between these fractions with words and pictures.

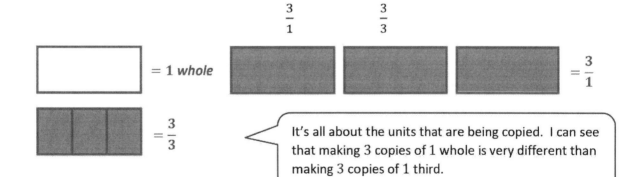

> It's all about the units that are being copied. I can see that making 3 copies of 1 whole is very different than making 3 copies of 1 third.

The fractions $\frac{3}{1}$ and $\frac{3}{3}$ are different because they both represent 3 copies, but the units that are copied are different. The fraction $\frac{3}{1}$ is 3 copies of 1 whole, and the fraction $\frac{3}{3}$ is 3 copies of 1 third. 3 copies of 1 whole, or $\frac{3}{1}$, is greater than 3 copies of 1 third, or $\frac{3}{3}$. My picture shows that $\frac{3}{1}$ is 3 wholes, and $\frac{3}{3}$ is only 1 whole.

G3-M5-Lesson 26

1. Partition the number line to show the fractional units. Then, draw number bonds with copies of 1 whole for the circled whole numbers.

I can partition the whole number intervals into fourths. I can count by fourths to label the fractions. I need to start at $\frac{8}{4}$ because this number line starts at 2.

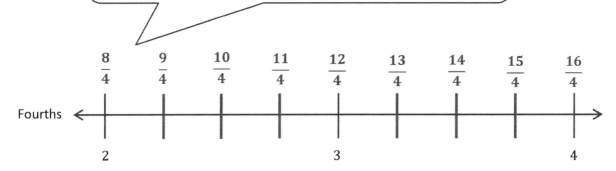

$2 = \underline{\ 8\ }$ fourths $3 = \underline{\ 12\ }$ fourths $4 = \underline{\ 16\ }$ fourths

$2 = \frac{8}{4}$ $3 = \frac{12}{4}$ $4 = \frac{16}{4}$

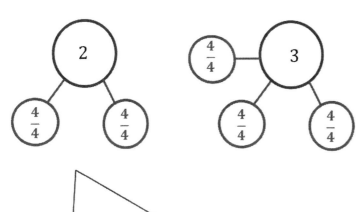

I can make copies of 1 whole to represent each whole number. Since the fractional unit is fourths, 1 whole can be represented by $\frac{4}{4}$. It takes 2 copies of $\frac{4}{4}$ to make the whole number 2.

Lesson 26:   Decompose whole number fractions greater than 1 using whole number
              equivalence with various models.

©2015 Great Minds. eureka-math.org
G3-M5-HWH-1.3.0-10.2015

EUREKA
MATH

2. Use the number line to write the fractions that name the whole numbers for each fractional unit. The first one has been done for you.

	2	3	4
Thirds	$\frac{6}{3}$	$\frac{9}{3}$	$\frac{12}{3}$
Sixths	$\frac{12}{6}$	$\frac{18}{6}$	$\frac{24}{6}$
Ninths	$\frac{18}{9}$	$\frac{27}{9}$	$\frac{36}{9}$

I know that $\frac{12}{6} = 2$. I can count by sixths to find the other fractions that name the whole numbers on the number line. I can do the same thing for ninths.

3. Monica walks $\frac{1}{4}$ of a mile on Monday. Each day after that, she walks $\frac{1}{4}$ of a mile more than she did the day before. Draw and partition a number line to represent how far Monica walks on Monday, Tuesday, Wednesday, and Thursday. What fraction of a mile does she walk on Thursday?

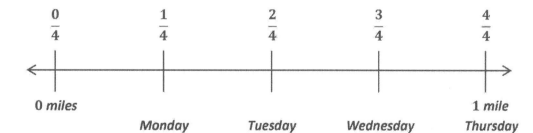

Monica walks $\frac{4}{4}$ of a mile on Thursday.

I can draw a number line and partition it into fourths because the fractional unit is fourths and Monica walks for 4 days. I can see on my number line that on Thursday Monica walks $\frac{4}{4}$ of a mile, which is the same as 1 mile.

EUREKA MATH   Lesson 26:   Decompose whole number fractions greater than 1 using whole number   43
                                 equivalence with various models.

                   ©2015 Great Minds. eureka-math.org
                   G3-M5-HWH-1.3.0-10.2015

G3-M5-Lesson 27

1. Use the pictures to model equivalent fractions. Fill in the blanks, and answer the questions.

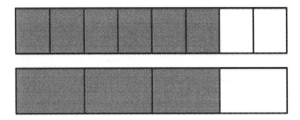

I can shade 6 eighths, and then I can shade fourths until the same amount in each model is shaded. It takes 3 fourths to equal 6 eighths.

6 eighths is equal to __3__ fourths.

$$\frac{6}{8} = \frac{3}{4}$$

The whole stays the same.

What happens to the size of the equal parts when there are fewer equal parts?

When there are fewer equal parts, the size of each equal part gets bigger. Fourths are bigger than eighths.

2. Six friends share 2 crackers that are both the same size. The crackers are represented by the 2 rectangles below. The first cracker is cut into 3 equal parts, and the second is cut into 6 equal parts. How can the 6 friends share the crackers equally without breaking any of the pieces?

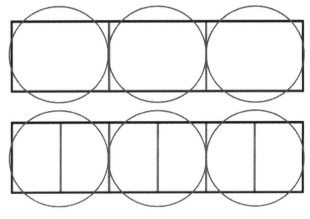

I can partition the first cracker into thirds and the second cracker into sixths. I can circle 6 equal amounts to show how much each friend gets.

Three friends each get $\frac{1}{3}$ of the first cracker. The other 3 friends each get $\frac{2}{6}$ of the second cracker.
They all get the same amount because $\frac{1}{3} = \frac{2}{6}$.

EUREKA
MATH™

3. Mrs. Mills cuts a pizza into 6 equal slices. Then, she cuts every slice in half. How many of the smaller slices does she have? Use words and numbers to explain your answer.

She has 12 smaller slices of pizza. Since she cut each slice in half, that means that she doubled the number of pieces and 6 × 2 = 12. The smaller the pieces, the more pieces it takes to make a whole.

> If I need to, I can draw a picture. I can draw a circle and partition it into sixths. Then, I can partition each sixth into 2 equal pieces. That would make 12 pieces.

©2015 Great Minds. eureka-math.org
G3-M5-HWH-1.3.0-10.2015

G3-M5-Lesson 28

1. Shade the models to compare the fractions.

2 fourths

2 eighths

Which is larger, 2 fourths or 2 eighths? Why? Use words to explain.

2 fourths is larger than 2 eighths because the more times you cut the whole, the smaller the pieces get. The number of pieces I shaded is the same, but the sizes of the pieces are different. Eighths are much smaller than fourths.

2. After baseball practice, Steven and Eric each buy a 1-liter bottle of water. Steven drinks 3 sixths of his water. Eric drinks 3 fourths of his water. Who drinks more water? Draw a picture to support your answer.

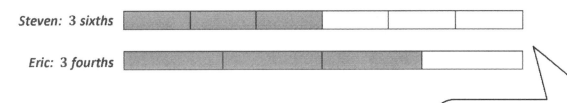

Steven: 3 sixths

Eric: 3 fourths

Eric drinks more water.

I can see from my picture that 3 fourths is greater than 3 sixths. I shaded the same number of parts, but the wholes are partitioned into different fractional units. Sixths are smaller than fourths.

Steven and Eric each buy a 1-liter bottle of water, so I need to draw my 2 wholes exactly the same size. If the size of the whole changes, I won't be able to accurately compare the 2 fractions.

©2015 Great Minds. eureka-math.org
G3-M5-HWH-1.3.0-10.2015

G3-M5-Lesson 29

1. Draw your own model to compare the following fractions. Then, complete the number sentence by writing >, <, or =.

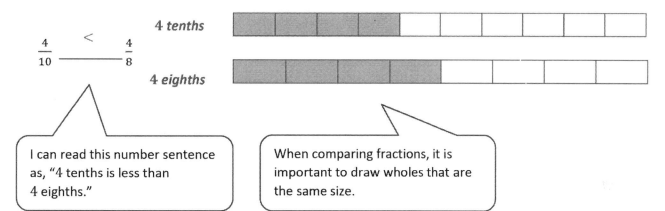

4 tenths

$$\frac{4}{10} \quad < \quad \frac{4}{8}$$

4 eighths

> I can read this number sentence as, "4 tenths is less than 4 eighths."

> When comparing fractions, it is important to draw wholes that are the same size.

2. Draw 2 number lines with endpoints 0 and 1 to show each fraction in Problem 1. Use the number lines to explain how you know your comparison in Problem 1 is correct.

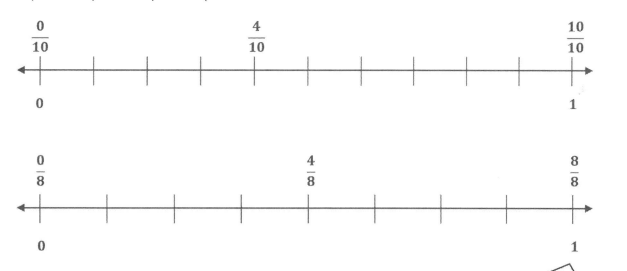

My answer in Problem 1 is correct. 4 tenths is less than 4 eighths because 4 tenths is a shorter distance from 0 than 4 eighths on the number line.

> I can see that 10 tenths and 8 eighths are equivalent fractions because they have the same point on the number line. This is also true for 0 tenths and 0 eighths.

Lesson 29:   Compare fractions with the same numerator using <, >, or =, and use a model to reason about their size.   47

©2015 Great Minds. eureka-math.org
G3-M5-HWH-1.3.0-10.2015

G3-M5-Lesson 30

Theodore precisely partitions his red strip into fifths using the number line method below. Describe step by step how Theodore partitions his strip into equal units using only a piece of notebook paper and a straight edge.

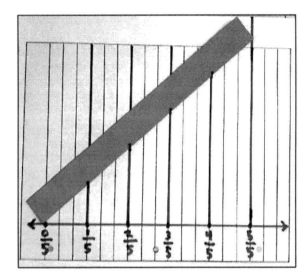

First, Theodore uses the paper's margin line to draw a number line. He then labels fifths on his number line from 0 to 1. He uses 3 spaces for each fifth. Next, at each fifth, he draws vertical lines up from the number line to the top of the paper. He then takes his red strip and angles it so that the left end touches the 0 endpoint on the number line, and the right end touches the line at 5 fifths, or 1. Finally, he marks on the red strip where the vertical points touch it. This creates equal units on the red strip. Theodore can double check by measuring them with a ruler.

Using this method, I can make fractional units precisely without a ruler. If I want to partition longer strips, like a meter strip, I tape more lined papers above the first one so that I can make a sharper angle with the longer strip.

Lesson 30:   Partition various wholes precisely into equal parts using a number line
method.

©2015 Great Minds. eureka-math.org
G3-M5-HWH-1.3.0-10.2015

EUREKA MATH

Homework Helpers

Grade 3
Module 6

G3-M6-Lesson 1

1. The tally chart below shows a survey of students' favorite ice cream flavors. Each tally mark represents 1 student.

Favorite Ice Cream Flavors	
Flavors	Number of Students
Chocolate	ⵁⵁⵁⵁ /
Vanilla	ⵁⵁⵁⵁ
Cookie Dough	ⵁⵁⵁⵁ //
Mint Chocolate Chip	////

> I can count the tally marks by fives and ones to find the total number of students.

The chart shows a total of ___22___ students.

2. Use the tally chart in Problem 1 to complete the picture graph below.

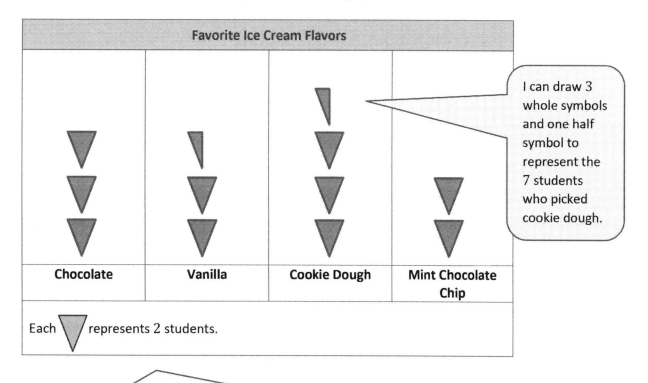

> I can draw 3 whole symbols and one half symbol to represent the 7 students who picked cookie dough.

Each ▽ represents 2 students.

> I can use the key to tell me what each symbol represents. Since each symbol represents 2 students, I can draw half a symbol to represent 1 student.

a. What does each ▽ represent?

> I can look at the key in the picture graph to find this information.

Each ▼ *represents 2 students.*

b. How many students picked vanilla as their favorite ice cream flavor?

Five students picked vanilla as their favorite ice cream flavor.

> I can look at the picture graph or the tally chart to figure out how many students picked vanilla. The picture graph shows 2 whole symbols and a half symbol, so that's 5 students.

c. How many more students chose cookie dough than mint chocolate chip as their favorite ice cream flavor?

$7 - 4 = 3$

Three more students chose cookie dough than mint chocolate chip.

> I can find the total for each flavor and subtract to find the difference.

d. How many students does  represent? Write a number sentence to show how you know.

$3 \times 2 = 6$

$6 + 1 = 7$

It represents 7 students.

> I can multiply 3×2 because there are 3 whole symbols, and each symbol stands for 2 students. Then, I can add 1 more because there is a half symbol, which represents 1 student.

e. How many more ▼ did you draw for chocolate than for mint chocolate chip? Write a number sentence to show how many more students chose chocolate than mint chocolate chip.

$6 - 4 = 2$

I drew 1 more symbol for chocolate than for mint chocolate chip.

> I can subtract to find the difference between the number of students who picked each flavor. The difference is 2 students. Since each symbol represents 2 students, that means I drew 1 more symbol for chocolate than for mint chocolate chip. I could also find the answer by looking at the chart and recognizing that 3 symbols for chocolate is 1 more than the 2 symbols I drew for mint chocolate chip.

Lesson 1:   Generate and organize data.   **EUREKA MATH**

©2015 Great Minds. eureka-math.org
G3-M6-HWH-1.3.0-10.2015

G3-M6-Lesson 2

1. Lenny surveys third graders to find out their favorite recess activities. The results are in the table below.

Favorite Recess Activities	
Recess Activity	Number of Student Votes
Swinging	6
Tag	10
Basketball	14
Kickball	8

Draw units of 2 to complete the tape diagrams to show the total votes for each recess activity. The first one has been done for you.

Swinging: | 2 | 2 | 2 |

Tag: | 2 | 2 | 2 | 2 | 2 |

Basketball: | 2 | 2 | 2 | 2 | 2 | 2 | 2 |

Kickball: | 2 | 2 | 2 | 2 |

> I can do my best to draw all of my units the same size because they all represent the same thing, 2 students. I can also make sure to line up each tape diagram with the one above it.

> When I make my units the same size and line up my tape diagrams, it makes it easy to compare the number of votes for each activity. I can easily see that most third graders picked basketball as their favorite recess activity.

2. Complete the vertical tape diagrams below using the data from Problem 1.

a.

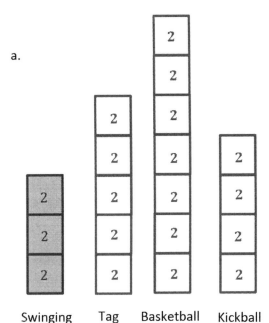

Swinging   Tag   Basketball   Kickball

I can rotate my tape diagrams from Problem 1 to create vertical tape diagrams. I still need to make sure my units are the same size and that the tape diagrams are lined up with each other.

b. What is a good title for the vertical tape diagrams?

A good title for the vertical tape diagrams is Favorite Recess Activities.

I can use the title from the table in Problem 1 as the title for the vertical tape diagrams because they both show the same information, just in different ways.

c. Write a multiplication sentence to show the total number of votes for basketball.

$7 \times 2 = 14$

There are 7 units of 2 for basketball, so I can represent the total with the multiplication sentence $7 \times 2 = 14$.

d. If the tape diagrams in Problem 1 were made with units of 1, how would your multiplication sentence in Problem 2(c) change?

If my tape diagrams were made with units of 1 instead of 2, the multiplication sentence for Problem 2(c) would be $14 \times 1 = 14$ because there would be 14 units of 1.

Since the value of each unit is less, I need a greater number of units to represent the same total.

4   Lesson 2:   Rotate tape diagrams vertically.

G3-M6-Lesson 3

1. This table shows the favorite seasons of third graders.

Favorite Seasons	
Season	Number of Student Votes
Fall	16
Winter	10
Spring	13
Summer	?

Use the table to color the bar graph.

The scale on the graph tells me that each square in the grid represents 2 students. To represent the number of students who picked fall, I can color 8 squares in the grid because $8 \times 2 = 16$.

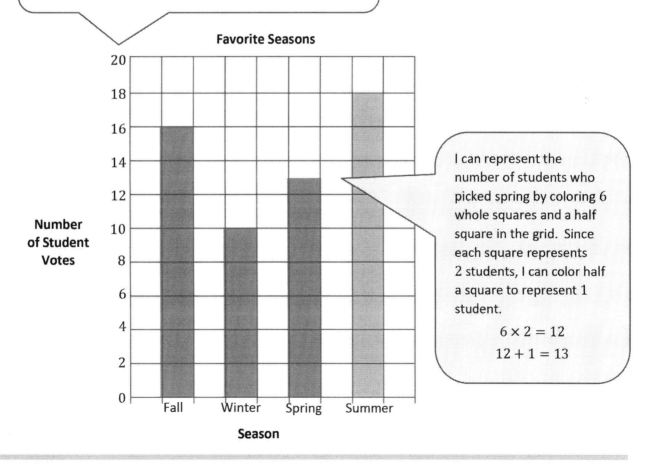

I can represent the number of students who picked spring by coloring 6 whole squares and a half square in the grid. Since each square represents 2 students, I can color half a square to represent 1 student.

$$6 \times 2 = 12$$
$$12 + 1 = 13$$

a.   How many students voted for summer?

   18 *students voted for summer.* ◁──┐ I can count by two on the bar graph to figure out how
                                          many students voted for summer.

b.   How many more students voted for fall than for spring? Write a number sentence to show your thinking.

   $16 - 13 = 3$ ◁──┐ I can subtract the number of students who voted for
                     spring from the number of students who voted for fall.

   3 more students voted for fall than for spring.

c.   Which combination of seasons gets more votes, fall and winter together or spring and summer together? Show your work.

   Fall and winter: $16 + 10 = 26$

   Spring and summer: $13 + 18 = 31$

   The combination of spring and summer together gets more votes than fall and winter together.

   I can add the votes for fall and winter to figure out how many students voted for those two seasons. Then I can do the same thing for spring and summer. I can compare the totals to figure out which combination of seasons gets more votes.

d.   How many third graders voted in all? Show your work.

   $16 + 10 + 13 + 18$
   $\vee$
   $26 + 13 + 18$
   $\vee$
   $39 + 18$
     $/ \backslash$
    $1 \quad 17$

   $39 + 1 = 40$
   $40 + 17 = 57$

   I can add the votes for all 4 seasons to find the total number of third graders who voted. Or, I can add the totals of fall and winter and spring and summer from Problem 1(c).
   $26 + 31 = 57$
   Either way, I get the same answer!

   57 third graders voted in all.

G3-M6-Lesson 4

1. Farmer Brown collects the data below about the cows on his farm.

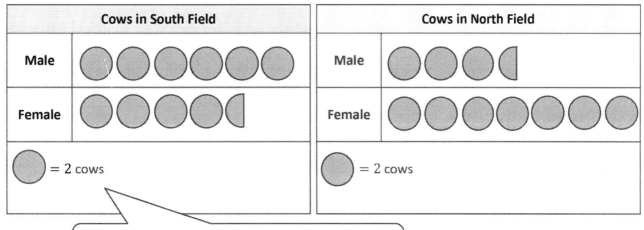

Cows in South Field		Cows in North Field	
Male	⬤⬤⬤⬤⬤⬤	Male	⬤⬤⬤◖
Female	⬤⬤⬤⬤◖	Female	⬤⬤⬤⬤⬤⬤
⬤ = 2 cows		⬤ = 2 cows	

> The key tells me that each circle represents 2 cows. That means that half a circle represents 1 cow.

a. How many fewer male cows does Farmer Brown have than female cows?

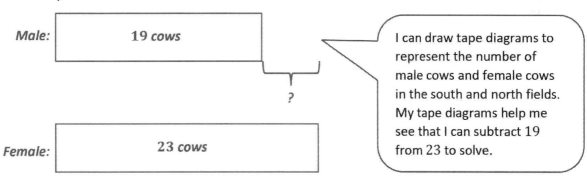

Male: 19 cows

?

Female: 23 cows

> I can draw tape diagrams to represent the number of male cows and female cows in the south and north fields. My tape diagrams help me see that I can subtract 19 from 23 to solve.

$23 - 19 = ?$

$24 - 20 = 4$

> I can use compensation to subtract. When I add 1 to each number, I have a much easier problem to solve!

Farmer Brown has 4 fewer male cows than female cows.

b. It takes Farmer Brown 10 minutes to milk each female cow. How many minutes does he spend milking all of the female cows?

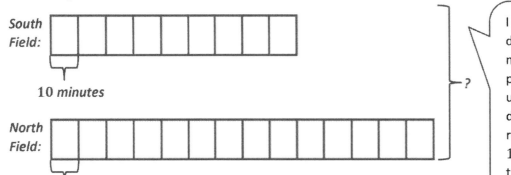

South Field:

10 *minutes*

North Field:

10 *minutes*

?

I can draw tape diagrams to model the problem. Each unit in the tape diagrams represents the 10 minutes it takes to milk 1 cow.

$23 \times 10 = ?$

$(20 \times 10) + (3 \times 10) =$

$200 + 30 = 230$

I can see in my tape diagrams that there are 23 units of 10, which I can represent with 23×10. I can use the break apart and distribute strategy to solve. Or I can find the total minutes for the cows in each field and then add.

Farmer Brown spends 230 *minutes milking all of the female cows.*

c. Farmer Brown's barn has 6 rows of stalls with 8 stalls in each row. How many empty stalls will there be when all the cows are in the barn?

?

8 *stalls*

I can draw a tape diagram to model the rows of stalls in the barn. I can multiply to find the total number of stalls.

$6 \times 8 = 48$

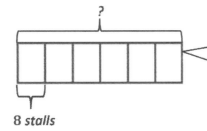

$23 + 19 = ?$

22   1

I know there are 19 male cows and 23 female cows from my work in Problem 1(a). I can add to find the total number of cows, 42. Then, I can subtract the number of cows from the number of stalls to solve for the number of empty stalls.

$19 + 1 = 20$

$20 + 22 = 42$

$48 - 42 = 6$ *There are* 6 *empty stalls when all of the cows are in the barn.*

EUREKA MATH

G3-M6-Lesson 5

1. Samantha measures 3 crayons to the nearest inch, $\frac{1}{2}$ inch, and $\frac{1}{4}$ inch. She records the measurements in the chart below.

Crayon (color)	Measured to the Nearest Inch	Measured to the Nearest $\frac{1}{2}$ Inch	Measured to the Nearest $\frac{1}{4}$ Inch
Orange	4	$4\frac{1}{2}$	$4\frac{3}{4}$
Pink	2	$2\frac{1}{2}$	$2\frac{1}{2}$
Blue	6	6	$5\frac{3}{4}$

a. Which crayon is the longest? _____blue_____

   It measures ___$5\frac{3}{4}$___ inches. ◁─── The blue crayon was measured 3 times, but the most precise measurement is $5\frac{3}{4}$ inches.

b. Look carefully at Samantha's data. Which crayon most likely needs to be measured again? Explain how you know.

   The orange crayon most likely needs to be measured again. Samantha recorded 4 inches as the measurement to the nearest inch and $4\frac{3}{4}$ inches as the measurement to the nearest $\frac{1}{4}$ inch. Those measurements don't make sense. If the crayon really measures close to $4\frac{3}{4}$ inches, then the measurement to the nearest inch would be 5 inches, not 4 inches.

   $4\frac{3}{4}$ inches is only $\frac{1}{4}$ inch away from 5 inches. It doesn't make sense for the same crayon to have measurements of $4\frac{3}{4}$ inches and 4 inches.

Lesson 5:   Create ruler with 1-inch, $\frac{1}{2}$ inch, and $\frac{1}{4}$ inch intervals, and generate measurement data.

©2015 Great Minds. eureka-math.org
G3-M6-HWH-1.3.0-10.2015

9

2. Evelyn marks a 3-inch paper strip into equal parts as shown below.

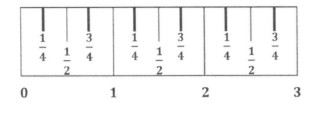

I can start at the edge of the paper strip and label it 0 inches. Then I can label the rest of the whole inches. I can label the mark halfway between each whole inch as $\frac{1}{2}$ inch.

a. Label the whole and half inches on the paper strip.

b. Estimate to draw the $\frac{1}{4}$ inch marks on the paper strip. Then, fill in the blanks below.

2 inches are equal to __4__ half inches.

2 inches are equal to __8__ quarter inches.

2 half inches are equal to __4__ quarter inches.

4 quarter inches are equal to __2__ half inches.

I can estimate to partition each $\frac{1}{2}$ inch into 2 equal parts to mark and label the $\frac{1}{4}$ inches. Then I can use the strip to help me fill in the blanks.

3. Samantha says her pink crayon measures $2\frac{1}{2}$ inches. Daniel says that's the same as 5 half inches. Explain how they are both correct.

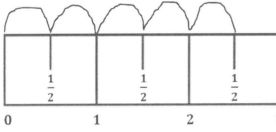

I can see in my drawing that there are 5 half inches in $2\frac{1}{2}$ inches.

They are both correct because there are 2 half inches in each inch, so $2\frac{1}{2}$ inches is equal to 5 half inches.

G3-M6-Lesson 6

Mr. Jackson records the amount of time his piano students spend practicing in one week. The times are shown on the line plot below.

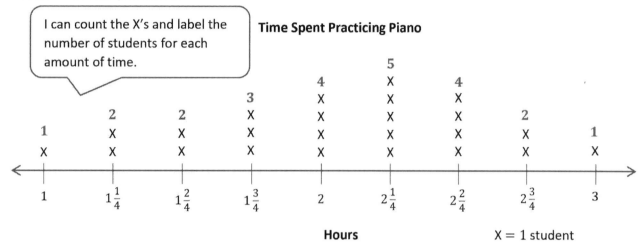

a. How many students practiced for 2 hours?

   4 students practiced for 2 hours.

   I can look at the labels I put on the line plot after counting to easily answer this question.

b. How many students take piano lessons from Mr. Jackson? How do you know?

   24 students take lessons from Mr. Jackson. I know because I counted all of the X's on the line plot.

   I can count the X's, or I can add all of the numbers that I labeled on the line plot.
   $1 + 2 + 2 + 3 + 4 + 5 + 4 + 2 + 1 = 24$

c. How many students practiced for more than $2\frac{2}{4}$ hours?

   3 students practiced for more than $2\frac{2}{4}$ hours.

   Since it says more than $2\frac{2}{4}$ hours, I can just count the X's for $2\frac{3}{4}$ hours and 3 hours.

d. Mr. Jackson says that for students to participate in the recital, they must practice for at least 2 hours. How many students can participate in the recital?

16 students can participate in the recital.

> I can count the X's for the times that are equal to or more than 2 hours because the problems says, "at least 2 hours."

e. Mr. Jackson notices that the 3 most frequent times spent practicing are 2 hours, $2\frac{1}{4}$ hours, and $2\frac{2}{4}$ hours. Do you agree? Explain your answer.

Yes, I agree. 4 students practiced for both 2 hours and $2\frac{2}{4}$ hours, and 5 students practiced for $2\frac{1}{4}$ hours. These numbers of students, 4 and 5, are the most for any of the times practiced.

> I know that "most frequent times" means the times that most students spend practicing.

f. Mr. Jackson says that the most common time spent practicing is 10 quarter hours. Is he right? Why or why not?

No, he's not right. The most common time spent practicing is $2\frac{1}{4}$ hours. Since there are 4 quarter hours in each hour, there are 9 quarter hours in $2\frac{1}{4}$ hours.

$2 \times 4 = 8$

$8 + 1 = 9$

> I know that the most common time spent practicing is $2\frac{1}{4}$ hours. I find the number of quarter hours in $2\frac{1}{4}$ hours first by multiplying 2×4 because there are 2 hours, and each hour is made up of 4 quarter hours. Then I can add $8 + 1$ because there is 1 more quarter hour in the time $2\frac{1}{4}$ hours. That makes 9 quarter hours.

12   Lesson 6:   Interpret measurement data from various line plots.

EUREKA MATH

G3-M6-Lesson 7

1. The table below shows the amount of time students in Mrs. Bishop's class spent doing homework on Monday night.

Hours Spent Doing Homework				
$1\frac{1}{4}$ ✓	$\frac{3}{4}$ ✓	$\frac{1}{4}$ ✓	$\frac{1}{2}$ ✓	$1\frac{1}{2}$ ✓
$\frac{3}{4}$ ✓	1 ✓	$\frac{3}{4}$ ✓	1 ✓	$\frac{1}{2}$ ✓
0 ✓	$\frac{1}{2}$ ✓	$\frac{3}{4}$ ✓	$\frac{1}{2}$ ✓	$\frac{3}{4}$ ✓
1 ✓	$\frac{1}{4}$ ✓	$\frac{1}{4}$ ✓	1 ✓	$1\frac{1}{4}$ ✓

I can draw a checkmark next to each time after I plot it. That way, I can be sure to plot each time only once.

a. Use the data to complete the line plot below.

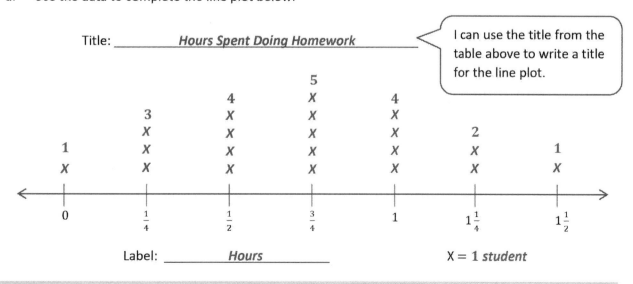

Title: _____ Hours Spent Doing Homework _____

I can use the title from the table above to write a title for the line plot.

```
                              5
                    4         X         4
          3         X         X         X
          X         X         X         X              2
1         X         X         X         X              X        1
X         X         X         X         X              X        X
←———————+—————————+—————————+—————————+—————————+—————————+————→
  0        1/4       1/2       3/4       1       1 1/4     1 1/2
```

Label: _____ Hours _____   X = 1 student

b. How many students spent $\frac{1}{2}$ hour doing their homework?

4 students spent $\frac{1}{2}$ hour doing their homework.

> I can count the X's for $\frac{1}{2}$ hour to answer this question.

c. How many students spent less than 1 hour doing their homework?

13 *students spent less than 1 hour doing their homework.*

> I can count the X's for 0 hours, $\frac{1}{4}$ hour, $\frac{1}{2}$ hour, and $\frac{3}{4}$ hours because these times are all less than 1 hour.

d. How many students in Mrs. Bishop's class spent time doing homework on Monday night? How do you know?

19 *students in Mrs. Bishop's class spent time doing homework on Monday night. I know because I counted all of the X's except the X for 0 hours because that student didn't spend any time doing homework Monday night.*

> This problem was a little tricky because usually for a problem like this I can just count all of the X's. I can't count all of the X's this time because 1 student spent 0 hours doing homework on Monday night.

e. Kathleen says most students spent at least 1 hour doing their homework. Is she correct? Explain your thinking.

No, Kathleen is not correct. 7 students spent at least 1 hour doing their homework, but 13 students spent less than 1 hour doing their homework. Kathleen could say that most students spent less than 1 hour doing their homework.

> I can count the X's for 1 hour, $1\frac{1}{4}$ hours, and $1\frac{1}{2}$ hours to figure out how many students spent at least 1 hour doing their homework. I can look at my answer to Problem 1(c) to see how many students spent less than 1 hour doing their homework.

EUREKA MATH

©2015 Great Minds. eureka-math.org
G3-M6-HWH-1.3.0-10.2015

G3-M6-Lesson 8

Samuel is training his frog to compete in the frog-jumping contest at the county fair. The table below shows the distances that Samuel's frog jumped during his training time.

Distance Jumped (in Inches)				
$73\frac{3}{4}$ ✓	74 ✓	$74\frac{1}{4}$ ✓	74 ✓	$73\frac{1}{2}$ ✓
$74\frac{1}{2}$ ✓	$74\frac{1}{4}$ ✓	$74\frac{1}{2}$ ✓	$73\frac{3}{4}$ ✓	74 ✓
$73\frac{1}{4}$ ✓	$\boxed{74\frac{3}{4}}$ ✓	$\boxed{73}$ ✓	$74\frac{1}{4}$ ✓	$73\frac{1}{2}$ ✓
74 ✓	$73\frac{3}{4}$ ✓	74 ✓	74 ✓	$74\frac{1}{4}$ ✓

I can circle the shortest and longest distances to find the endpoints for my line plot.

a. Use the data to create a line plot below.

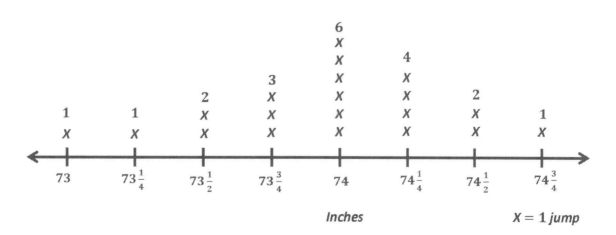

Distance Jumped

Inches   *X = 1 jump*

b. Explain the steps you took to create the line plot.

I found the endpoints by finding the shortest and longest distances, 73 inches and $74\frac{3}{4}$ inches.

Then I figured out what interval I should use on my line plot by finding the smallest unit, $\frac{1}{4}$ inch.

I marked the endpoints and partitioned and labeled quarter-inch intervals. Then I recorded the data by drawing X's above each measurement. I wrote a title, made a key, and labeled the measurements as Inches.

> I can count by quarter inches from 73 inches to $74\frac{3}{4}$ inches to figure out how many quarter-inch intervals I need on my line plot.

c. How many more times did Samuel's frog jump $74\frac{1}{4}$ inches than $73\frac{1}{2}$ inches?

$4 - 2 = 2$

> I can subtract the number of times the frog jumped $73\frac{1}{2}$ inches from the number of times the frog jumped $74\frac{1}{4}$ inches.

Samuel's frog jumped $74\frac{1}{4}$ inches 2 more times than it jumped $73\frac{1}{2}$ inches.

d. Find the three most frequent measurements on the line plot. What does this tell you about the distance of most of the frog's jumps?

The three most frequent measurements on the line plot are $73\frac{3}{4}$ inches, 74 inches, and $74\frac{1}{4}$ inches. This tells me that most of the frog's jumps were between $73\frac{3}{4}$ inches and $74\frac{1}{4}$ inches.

> I can prove this is true by subtracting the number of times the frog jumped $73\frac{3}{4}$ inches, 74 inches, or $74\frac{1}{4}$ inches from the total number of times the frog jumped.
>
> $20 - 13 = 7$
>
> Thirteen of the frog's jumps were between $73\frac{3}{4}$ inches and $74\frac{1}{4}$ inches. Seven of the jumps were not part of the three most frequent measurements.

EUREKA
MATH

©2015 Great Minds. eureka-math.org
G3-M6-HWH-1.3.0-10.2015

G3-M6-Lesson 9

1. The table below shows the amount of money Mrs. Mack's children have in their piggy banks.

Child	Amount of Money
Marie	$16
Nathan	$12
Mara	$15
Noah	$11

Create a picture graph below using the data in the table.

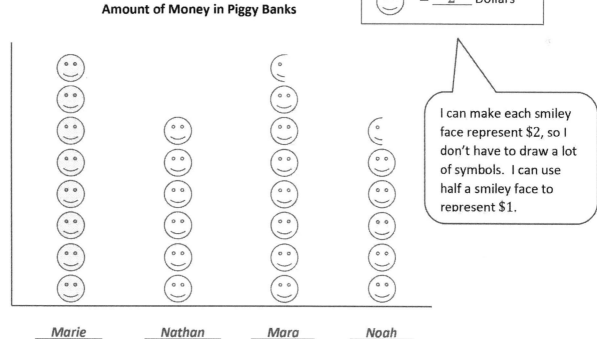

I can make each smiley face represent $2, so I don't have to draw a lot of symbols. I can use half a smiley face to represent $1.

2. Use the table or graph to answer the following questions.

   a. How much more money do Marie and Nathan have together than Mara and Noah have together?

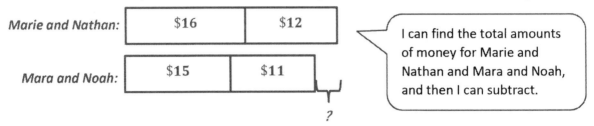

   $28 - $26 = $2   *Marie and Nathan have $2 more than Mara and Noah.*

   b. Marie and Noah combine their money to buy packs of baseball cards. Each pack of baseball cards costs $3. How many packs of baseball cards can they buy?

   $16 + $11 = $27

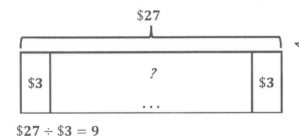

   $27 ÷ $3 = 9

   Marie and Noah can buy 9 packs of baseball cards.

   c. Mara gets $20 for her birthday. She combines her birthday money with the money in her piggy bank to buy a book for $9 and a bouquet of flowers for her mom. She puts the $8 that she has left back in her piggy bank. How much does the bouquet of flowers cost?

   $20 + $15 = $35

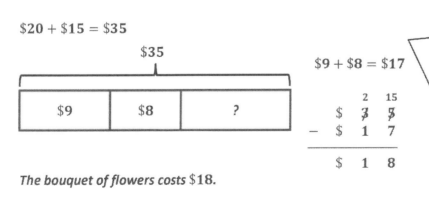

   The bouquet of flowers costs $18.

Homework Helpers

Grade 3
Module 7

G3-M7-Lesson 1

1. A museum uses 6 trucks to move paintings and sculptures to a new location. They move a total of 24 paintings and 18 sculptures. Each truck carries an equal number of paintings and an equal number of sculptures. How many paintings and how many sculptures are in each truck?

> I can use the Read-Draw-Write (RDW) process to solve. As I read the problem, I can visualize a picture of the problem in my mind. I know it's helpful to reread the problem in case I missed anything or didn't understand the information completely. Then I can ask myself, "What can I draw?"

24

paintings | p | | | | | |

> p represents the number of paintings in each truck
>
> $24 \div 6 = p$
> $p = 4$

18

sculptures | n | | | | | |

> n represents the number of sculptures in each truck
>
> $18 \div 6 = n$
> $n = 3$

> I can figure out what information is known and unknown using my drawing. I can represent my unknowns using letters. I know there are a total of 24 paintings and 18 sculptures. They are equally placed into 6 trucks. I know the totals and that the number of groups is 6. So my unknown is the size of each group.

> Next, I can write number sentences based on my drawings.

> The final step of the Read-Draw-Write (RDW) process is to write a sentence with words to answer the problem. I can reread the question to be sure that my sentence answers it. This also gives me a chance to look back at my calculation to make sure that my answer is reasonable.

There are 4 paintings and 3 sculptures in each truck.

Lesson 1:   Solve word problems in varied contexts using a letter to represent the unknown.

©2015 Great Minds. eureka-math.org
G3-M7-HWH-1.3.0-10.2015

2. Christopher's father gives the cashier $30 to pay for 7 keychains from the gift shop. The cashier gives him $9 in change. How much does each keychain cost?

> I know there are many ways to draw and solve this problem, but I want to draw a model that is most helpful to me.

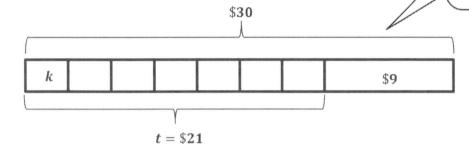

t represents the total cost of 7 keychains

$$\$30 - \$9 = t$$
$$t = \$21$$

k represents the cost of each keychain

$$\$21 \div 7 = k$$
$$k = \$3$$

Each keychain costs $3.

> This time I choose to draw only one tape diagram and label both unknowns with letters. I know I first need to solve for t, and then I can solve for k. Labeling the unknowns with different letters helps me differentiate the two unknowns easily.

> Now I can write my number sentences and a statement that answers the question.

Lesson 1:   Solve word problems in varied contexts using a letter to represent the unknown.

EUREKA MATH

G3-M7-Lesson 2

Kathy is 167 centimeters tall. The total height of Kathy and her younger sister Jenny is 319 centimeters. How much taller is Kathy than Jenny? Draw at least 2 different ways to represent the problem.

> I can use the RDW process to help me solve. First, I need to read (and reread) the problem. This will help me visualize the problem. Then, I can draw a model to represent the problem with the known and unknown information.

Step 1:

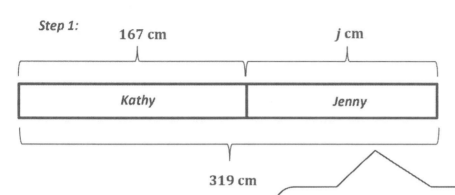

j represents Jenny's height in centimeters

$$319 \text{ cm} - 167 \text{ cm} = j$$
$$j = 152 \text{ cm}$$

> I notice that this is a two-step problem. From my drawing, I know the total height of the two sisters and the height of Kathy. The unknown in my drawing is Jenny's height, which is labeled with the letter j. I can write a subtraction equation to find her height. But this doesn't answer the question.

Step 2:

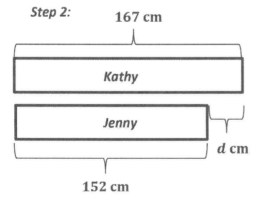

d represents the difference between the two heights in centimeters

$$167 \text{ cm} - 152 \text{ cm} = d$$
$$d = 15 \text{ cm}$$

> The question is, "How much taller is Kathy than Jenny?" That means I need to draw a second diagram and write a subtraction equation to answer the question. I can label the unknown, which this time is the difference of their heights, with a new letter.

> Finally, I can check my work when I write my statement.

Kathy is 15 centimeters taller than Jenny.

 Lesson 2: Solve word problems in varied contexts using a letter to represent the unknown.

©2015 Great Minds. eureka-math.org
G3-M7-HWH-1.3.0-10.2015

3

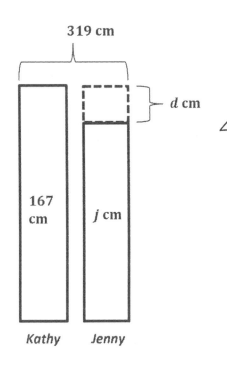

319 cm

167 cm

d cm

j cm

Kathy   Jenny

This is another way to represent the problem. I can draw my tape diagram vertically because the problem is about height. I can also put both unknowns in one diagram instead of drawing each step separately. This might save me time. The next step will be to write equations and a statement that go with my drawing.

I could also model the problem using number bonds because they show the part–part–whole relationship.

Step 1:

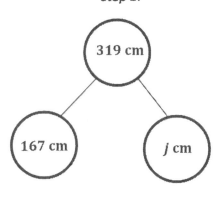

319 cm

167 cm   *j* cm

Step 2:

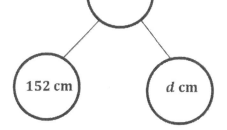

167 cm

152 cm   *d* cm

There are many different ways to label and model the same problem, but I always want to draw a model that represents the problem most clearly to me. My drawing is important because it helps me decide on a way to solve, and it also helps me write my number sentences and a written statement to answer the question.

Lesson 2:   Solve word problems in varied contexts using a letter to represent the unknown.

©2015 Great Minds. eureka-math.org
G3-M7-HWH-1.3.0-10.2015

EUREKA MATH

G3-M7-Lesson 3

I will use the RDW (Read-Draw-Write) process to solve this multi-step problem. First I'll read the problem, then I'll pause and visualize what's happening in the problem to get an idea about what to draw.

Mrs. Yoon buys 6 bags of counters. Nine counters come in each bag. She gives each of her 12 math students 4 counters. How many counters does she have left?

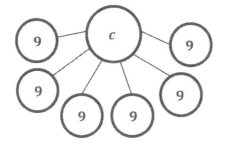

or

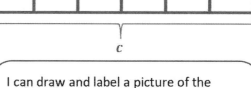

c represents the total number counters Mrs. Yoon buys.

$6 \times 9 = c$
$c = 54$

Mrs. Yoon buys 54 counters.

I can draw and label a picture of the problem in many different ways. Here's how I could use either a number bond or a tape diagram to show the first part of the problem. Both models show that the unknown is the whole, or the total.

g

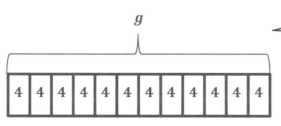

g represents the total number of counters Mrs. Yoon gives away.

$$g = 12 \times 4$$
$$= (10 + 2) \times 4$$
$$= (10 \times 4) + (2 \times 4)$$
$$= 40 + 8$$
$$g = 48$$

Mrs. Yoon gives away 48 counters.

$54 - 48 = 6$

Mrs. Yoon has 6 counters left.

Next, I can draw a second model to help me find the total number of counters Mrs. Yoon gives away. This time I can use g to represent the unknown.

To solve this larger fact I can break apart 12 as 10 and 2, then distribute the 4. I chose to break apart the 12 because tens facts are easy for me.

I can reread the question and see that my statement doesn't answer it. That helps me remember that there's one step left to do. I need to subtract the number of counters Mrs. Yoon gives away from her total counters to find how many she has left.

G3-M7-Lesson 4

1. Complete the chart by answering true or false.

Attribute	Polygon	True or False
Example: 3 Sides		True
Quadrilateral		*True*
2 Sets of Parallel Sides		*False*

> This is true. This shape has four sides and four angles. I know polygons with four straight sides and four angles are called quadrilaterals.

> This is false. This shape only has 1 set of parallel sides. I can think of parallel sides like the two side lines of a capital H, or a slanted *H*, since not all parallel sides stand vertical. Even if the two lines go on forever, they will never cross.

2. Use a straightedge to sketch 2 different quadrilaterals with at least 1 set of parallel sides.

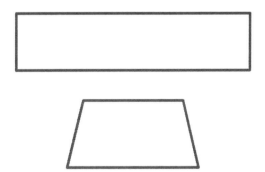

> I can draw a rectangle with 2 sets of parallel sides and a trapezoid with 1 set of parallel sides.

G3-M7-Lesson 5

1. Match the polygons with their appropriate banners. A polygon can match to more than one banner.

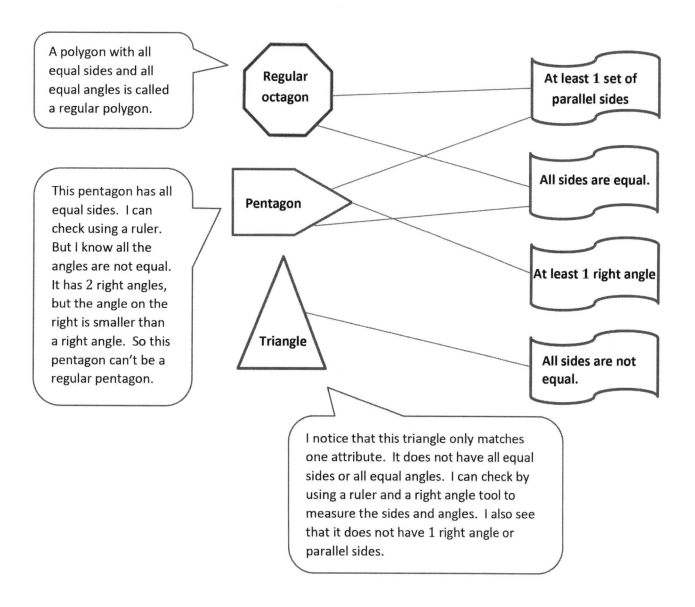

A polygon with all equal sides and all equal angles is called a regular polygon.

Regular octagon

At least 1 set of parallel sides

All sides are equal.

This pentagon has all equal sides. I can check using a ruler. But I know all the angles are not equal. It has 2 right angles, but the angle on the right is smaller than a right angle. So this pentagon can't be a regular pentagon.

Pentagon

At least 1 right angle

Triangle

All sides are not equal.

I notice that this triangle only matches one attribute. It does not have all equal sides or all equal angles. I can check by using a ruler and a right angle tool to measure the sides and angles. I also see that it does not have 1 right angle or parallel sides.

©2015 Great Minds. eureka-math.org
G3-M7-HWH-1.3.0-10.2015

2. Compare the two polygons below. What is the same? What is different?

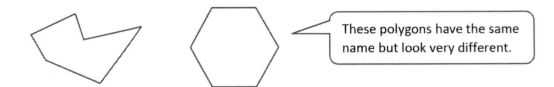

These polygons have the same name but look very different.

Both polygons have 6 sides, so they are both hexagons. The hexagon on the right is a regular hexagon because it has all equal sides and angles. The hexagon on the left does not have all equal sides and angles, so it is not a regular hexagon.

3. David draws the polygons below. Are any of them regular polygons? Explain how you know.

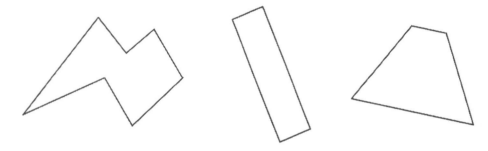

None of David's polygons are regular polygons. I know because I measured the sides and angles of each shape using my ruler and right angle tool, and none of these shapes have all equal sides and all equal angles.

My right angle tool is the corner of an index card. Using my measuring tools helps me to be precise.

EUREKA
MATH

G3-M7-Lesson 6

A right angle tool is just the corner of an index card.

Use a ruler and a right angle tool to help you draw the figures with the attributes given below.

1. Draw a triangle with all equal sides.

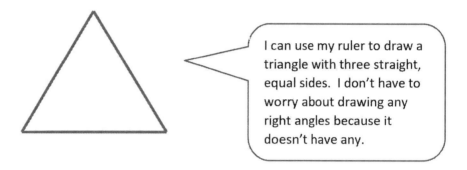

I can use my ruler to draw a triangle with three straight, equal sides. I don't have to worry about drawing any right angles because it doesn't have any.

2. Draw a quadrilateral with at least 1 set of parallel sides and at least 1 right angle. Mark the right angle and parallel sides.

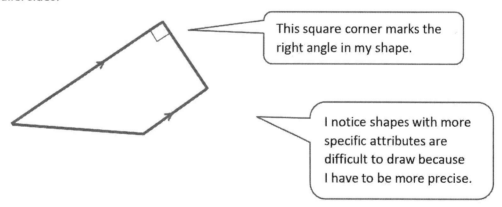

This square corner marks the right angle in my shape.

I notice shapes with more specific attributes are difficult to draw because I have to be more precise.

3. Melissa says she drew a polygon with 4 sides and 4 right angles with no parallel sides. Can Melissa be correct?

    Melissa can't be correct because there is no quadrilateral with 4 right angles and no parallel sides. Only rectangles and squares have 4 sides and 4 right angles, but they both have 2 sets of parallel sides.

G3-M7-Lesson 7

The directions tell me the area of each square has to be 16 square units. I can figure out how many tetrominoes I will need by dividing, 16 square units ÷ 4 square units = 4. I will need to use 4 tetrominoes for each square.

1. Use tetrominoes to create three squares, each with an area of 16 square units. Then, color the grid below to show how you created your squares. You may use the same tetromino more than once.

Tetrominoes

A tetromino is a shape that has an area of 4 square units, and each square unit shares a whole side with another square unit. This is a set of tetrominoes.

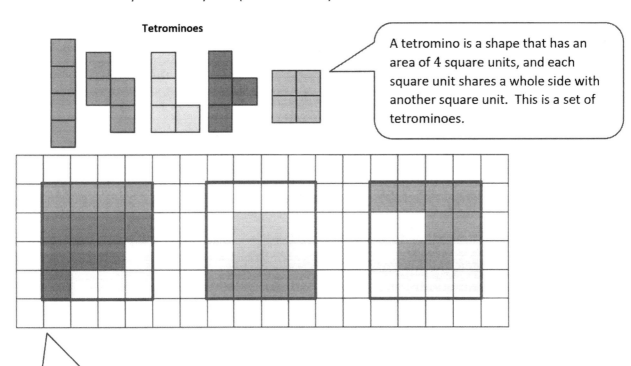

A strategy I can use to help me make a square with an area of 16 square units is by first marking a 4 by 4 square on the grid. This will help me make sure that my square has the right area. Then I can build the square with the tetrominoes. Sometimes I will need to rotate or flip my tetrominoes to build my shape.

I can check that my shapes are squares by counting the number of square units on each side and making sure they are all equal. I can also use my right angle tool to make sure that each shape has 4 right angles.

EUREKA MATH

©2015 Great Minds. eureka-math.org
G3-M7-HWH-1.3.0-10.2015

2. Explain how you know the area of each square is 16 square units.

I know the area of each square is 16 square units because I used 4 tetrominoes to make each square. Each tetromino has an area of 4 square units, and 4 × 4 square units = 16 square units.

a. Write a number sentence to show the area of a square from Problem 1 as the sum of the areas of the tetrominoes you used to make the square.

Area: 4 square units + 4 square units + 4 square units + 4 square units = 16 square units

b. Write a number sentence to show the area of a square above as the product of its side lengths.

Area: 4 units × 4 units = 16 square units

> I know side lengths are measured in length units, and area is labeled in square units.

> The directions say to write a number sentence that shows the area of a square as the sum of the areas of the tetrominoes, so I know that each of my addends is labeled in square units.

G3-M7-Lesson 8

1. Draw a line to divide the rectangle below into 2 equal triangles.

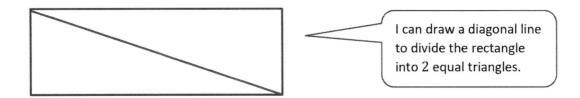

I can draw a diagonal line to divide the rectangle into 2 equal triangles.

2. Draw 2 lines to divide the quadrilateral below into 4 equal triangles.

I can draw 2 diagonal lines to divide this quadrilateral into 4 equal triangles.

3. Choose three shapes from your tangram puzzle. Trace them below. Describe *at least* one attribute that they have in common.

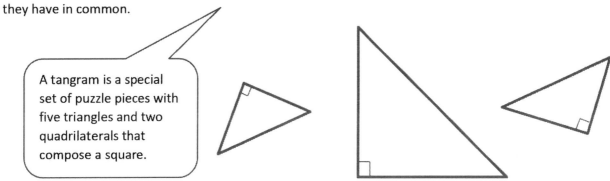

A tangram is a special set of puzzle pieces with five triangles and two quadrilaterals that compose a square.

All three shapes are triangles. They all have 1 right angle and 3 sides. None of the triangles have parallel sides.

G3-M7-Lesson 9

1. Use your two smallest triangles to create a triangle, a parallelogram, and a square. Show how you created them below.

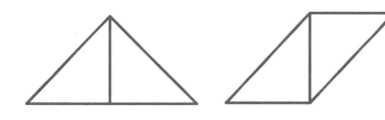

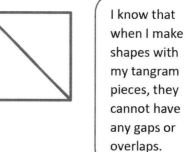

I know that when I make shapes with my tangram pieces, they cannot have any gaps or overlaps.

2. Use at least two tangram pieces to make and draw as many 4-sided polygons as you can. Draw lines to show where the tangram pieces meet.

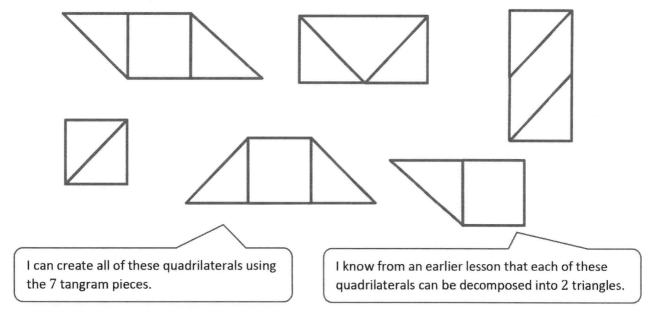

I can create all of these quadrilaterals using the 7 tangram pieces.

I know from an earlier lesson that each of these quadrilaterals can be decomposed into 2 triangles.

3. What attributes do your shapes in Problem 2 have in common? What attributes are different?

    All of the shapes I made in Problem 2 are quadrilaterals because they have 4 sides. They all have at least 1 set of parallel lines and 4 angles. Not all of my shapes have equal sides or right angles. That's what makes them different.

G3-M7-Lesson 10

1. Trace the perimeter of the shapes below with a black crayon. Then shade in the areas with a blue crayon.

2. Explain how you know you traced the perimeters of the shapes above. How is the perimeter different from the area of a shape?

    I know I traced the perimeters of the shapes because I traced the boundary of each shape with a black crayon, and the boundary is the perimeter. The area of a shape is different than the perimeter. Area measures the amount of space the shape takes up. I shaded the areas of the shapes in blue.

3. Explain how you could use a string to figure out which shape above has the greatest perimeter.

    I can wrap string around each shape and mark where it touches the end after going all around the boundary of the shape. Then I can compare all of the marks, and the shape with the mark farthest from the end of the string has the greatest perimeter.

Lesson 10:   Decompose quadrilaterals to understand perimeter as the boundary of a shape.   **EUREKA MATH**

©2015 Great Minds. eureka-math.org
G3-M7-HWH-1.3.0-10.2015

G3-M7-Lesson 11

1. Brian tessellates a parallelogram to make the shape below.

A tessellation is a figure made by copying a shape many times without any gaps or over laps.

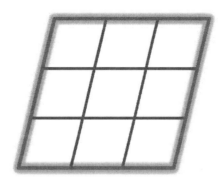

a. Outline the perimeter of Brian's new shape with a highlighter.

b. Name some attributes of his new shape.

    Brian's new shape is a quadrilateral because it has 4 sides. It has 2 sets of parallel lines and 4 angles, but none of them are right angles. Brian created a large parallelogram from smaller parallelograms.

c. Explain how Brian could use a string to measure the perimeter of his new shape.

    Brian could wrap his string around the boundary of his shape and mark where the string touches its end. Then he could measure up to the mark on his string using a ruler.

d. How could Brian increase the perimeter of his tessellation?

    Brian could increase the perimeter of his tessellation by tessellating more shapes. If he tessellated another row or column of shapes, that would increase the perimeter.

    I notice that the perimeter of the figure increases with each tessellation and decreases with taking away or erasing tessellations. I know that tessellations could go on forever, even past my paper!

 Lesson 11: Tessellate to understand perimeter as the boundary of a shape. (Optional.)   15

©2015 Great Minds. eureka-math.org
G3-M7-HWH-1.3.0-10.2015

2. Estimate to draw at least four copies of the given pentagon to make a new shape without gaps or overlaps. Outline the perimeter of your new shape with a highlighter.

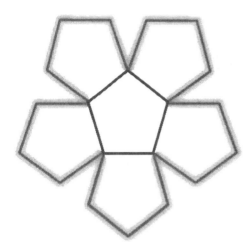

If my tessellations have overlaps or gaps, the shapes wouldn't fit together and the perimeter would not be accurate.

3. The marks on the strings below show the perimeters of Nancy's and Allen's shapes. Whose shape has a greater perimeter? How do you know?

Nancy's String:

Allen's String:

Nancy's shape has a greater perimeter. The mark on the string represents the perimeter of her shape, and it's farther down the string than Allen's mark.

It's just like how I compare numbers on the number line. I can pretend that the end of the string is like zero on the number line. Allen's mark is to the left of Nancy's, so Allen's is smaller because it is a shorter distance from 0.

EUREKA
MATH™

G3-M7-Lesson 12

1. Measure and label the side lengths of the shapes below in centimeters. Then, find the perimeter of each shape.

   a.

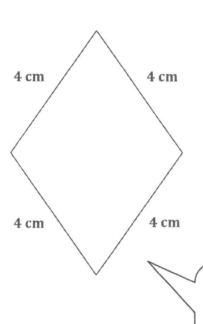

4 cm   4 cm

4 cm   4 cm

> I know the sides of a shape form the boundary, or perimeter, of the shape. I can use a ruler to measure and label the side lengths of this shape in centimeters. Then I can add all of the side lengths together to find the perimeter.

Perimeter $= 4 \text{ cm} + 4 \text{ cm} + 4 \text{ cm} + 4 \text{ cm}$

$= 16 \text{ cm}$

> I notice this shape is a quadrilateral with 4 equal sides and no right angles. That means it's a rhombus!

> I can also write this number sentence as $4 \times 4 \text{ cm} = 16 \text{ cm}$.

   b.

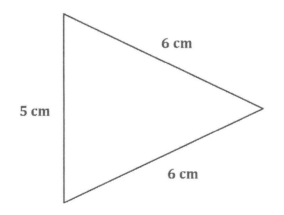

6 cm

5 cm

6 cm

Perimeter $= 5 \text{ cm} + 6 \text{ cm} + 6 \text{ cm}$

$= 17 \text{ cm}$

> It's important to label all of my measurements with the correct unit.

EUREKA MATH

Lesson 12: Measure side lengths in whole number units to determine the perimeter of polygons.

17

©2015 Great Minds. eureka-math.org
G3-M7-HWH-1.3.0-10.2015

2. Albert measures the two side lengths of the rectangle shown below. He says he can find the perimeter with the measurements. Explain Albert's thinking. Then, find the perimeter in centimeters.

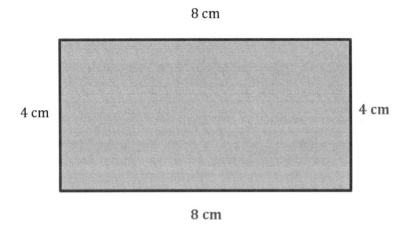

8 cm

4 cm   4 cm

8 cm

Albert can find the perimeter using the two side lengths he measured because opposite sides of a rectangle are equal. Since he knows the lengths of the two sides, he knows the lengths of the other two sides. Now he can find the perimeter.

$$\text{Perimeter} = 4\text{ cm} + 8\text{ cm} + 4\text{ cm} + 8\text{ cm}$$
$$= 24\text{ cm}$$

> I can also think of this problem as 3 eights = 24, or 12 + 12 = 24.

The perimeter of the rectangle is 24 centimeters.

©2015 Great Minds. eureka-math.org
G3-M7-HWH-1.3.0-10.2015

G3-M7-Lesson 13

1. Find the perimeter of the following shapes.

I see that the side lengths of each shape are already given, so I do not need to measure them. Now I just need to add the side lengths to find the perimeter.

a.

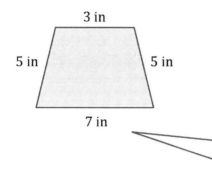

3 in

5 in   5 in

7 in

$P = 3 \text{ in} + 5 \text{ in} + 5 \text{ in} + 7 \text{ in}$

$P = 20 \text{ in}$

This quadrilateral has 1 set of parallel lines and no right angles. It's a trapezoid.

b.

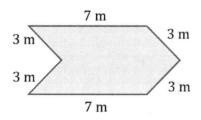

7 m

3 m   3 m

3 m

3 m

7 m

$P = 3 \text{ m} + 3 \text{ m} + 7 \text{ m} + 3 \text{ m} + 7 \text{ m} + 3 \text{ m}$

$P = 26 \text{ m}$

This shape has six sides, so it's a hexagon. It is not a regular hexagon because it does not have all equal sides.

I notice that each shape uses different units to measure. I need to make sure to label my measurements and their units correctly.

2. Allyson's rectangular garden is 31 feet long and 49 feet wide. What is the perimeter of Allyson's garden?

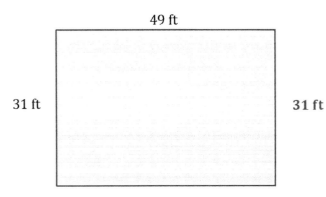

49 ft

31 ft   31 ft

49 ft

$P = 31 \text{ ft} + 49 \text{ ft} + 31 \text{ ft} + 49 \text{ ft}$

$P = 160 \text{ ft}$

I can use mental math to solve. I think of this problem as 30 ft + 50 ft + 30 ft + 50 ft since 1 less than 31 is 30 and 1 more than 49 is 50. 50 ft + 50 ft = 100 ft. Then, I just need to add 60 ft more because 30 ft + 30 ft = 60 ft.

I know the lengths of the other two sides because opposite sides of a rectangle are equal.

The perimeter of Allyson's garden is 160 feet.

Lesson 13:   Explore perimeter as an attribute of plane figures and solve problems.

©2015 Great Minds. eureka-math.org
G3-M7-HWH-1.3.0-10.2015

G3-M7-Lesson 14

1. Label the unknown side lengths of the regular shapes below. Then, find the perimeter of each shape.

    a.

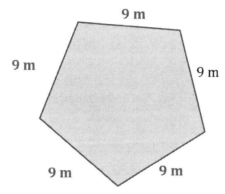

> Since this shape is a regular pentagon, I know that all the side lengths are equal. So each of the 5 sides measures 9 m.

Perimeter = 5 × 9 m = 45 m

> I can write a repeated addition sentence to find the perimeter, but a multiplication sentence is more efficient. I can write 5 × 9 m. 5 represents the number of sides, and 9 m is the length of each side.

    b.

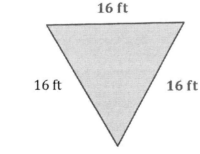

Perimeter = 3 × 16 ft

      = (3 × 10 ft) + (3 × 6 ft)

      = 30 ft + 18 ft

      = 48 ft

> I can use the break apart and distribute strategy to solve for a large fact like 3 × 16 ft. I can break apart 16 ft as 10 ft and 6 ft since multiplying by tens is easy. Then I can add the two smaller facts to find the answer to the larger fact.

EUREKA MATH   Lesson 14:   Determine the perimeter of regular polygons and rectangles when   21
whole number measurements are unknown.

©2015 Great Minds. eureka-math.org
G3-M7-HWH-1.3.0-10.2015

2. Jake traces a regular octagon on his paper. Each side measures 6 centimeters. He also traces a regular decagon on his paper. Each side of the decagon measures 4 centimeters. Which shape has a greater perimeter? Show your work.

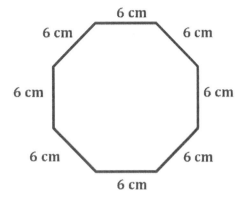

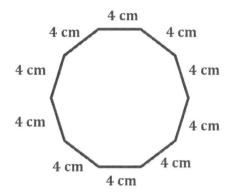

Perimeter = 8 × 6 cm = 48 cm   Perimeter = 10 × 4 cm = 40 cm

Jake's octagon has a greater perimeter by 8 cm.

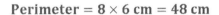

Even though a decagon has more sides than an octagon, the side lengths of Jake's octagon are longer than the side lengths of his decagon. That's why Jake's octagon has a greater perimeter.

EUREKA
MATH

©2015 Great Minds. eureka-math.org
G3-M7-HWH-1.3.0-10.2015

G3-M7-Lesson 15

1. Mr. Kim builds a 7 ft by 9 ft rectangular fence around his vegetable garden. What is the total length of Mr. Kim's fence?

I know that I need to draw and label a rectangle to represent Mr. Kim's fence. I can label all the side lengths of my rectangle because I know that opposite sides of a rectangle are equal.

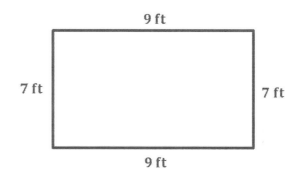

There are different strategies to find the perimeter of this rectangle. I could add 7 and 9 and then double the sum, or I can multiply each side length by 2 and then add the products just like I did here.

$$P = (2 \times 7\ \text{ft}) + (2 \times 9\ \text{ft})$$
$$= 14\ \text{ft} + 18\ \text{ft}$$
$$= 32\ \text{ft}$$

The total length of Mr. Kim's fence is 32 feet.

2. Gracie uses regular triangles to make the shape below. Each side length of a triangle measures 4 cm. What is the perimeter of Gracie's shape?

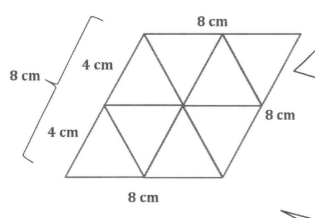

I know that each side length of the regular triangle is 4 cm. Since each side length of Gracie's larger shape is made up of 2 sides of a triangle, the side length of the larger shape is 8 cm. Now I can find the perimeter of her shape by writing a repeated addition sentence or multiplying the 4 side lengths by 8 cm.

$$P = 4 \times 8\ \text{cm} = 32\ \text{cm}$$

The perimeter of Gracie's shape is 32 cm.

Gracie's new shape has 4 equal sides and no right angles. It's a rhombus!

G3-M7-Lesson 16

1. Alicia draws the shape below.

    I know shapes that don't have straight lines, like circles, still have a perimeter. But I can't just use rulers to find their perimeters. I can estimate by using a string to represent the perimeter and then measure the string.

    a. Explain how Alicia could use string and a ruler to find the shape's perimeter.

        Alicia can wrap string around the boundary of her shape. Then, she can mark where the string meets the end after going all the way around once. Finally, she can use a ruler to measure from the end of the string to the mark.

        I know this method does not give me an exact perimeter since I am using string. It is a close estimate.

    b. Would you use this method to find the perimeter of a rectangle? Explain why or why not.

        I would not use this method to find the perimeter of a rectangle. Using string is not as efficient or as precise as measuring the sides of a rectangle with a ruler and then adding the side lengths together.

2. Can you find the perimeter of the shape below using just your ruler? Explain your answer.

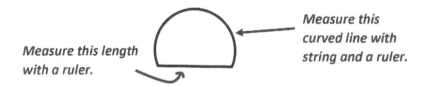

    Measure this length with a ruler.

    Measure this curved line with string and a ruler.

    No, I can't find the perimeter of the shape using just my ruler. The boundary of the shape has a curved line, and I can't measure curved lines with just a ruler. I can measure the straight side length with a ruler and use string to measure the curved line. Then, I can add the two measurements together to find the perimeter.

Lesson 16:   Use string to measure the perimeter of various circles to the nearest quarter inch.

©2015 Great Minds. eureka-math.org
G3-M7-HWH-1.3.0-10.2015

EUREKA MATH™

G3-M7-Lesson 17

1. The shape below is made up of rectangles. Label the unknown side lengths. Then, write and solve an equation to find the perimeter of the shape.

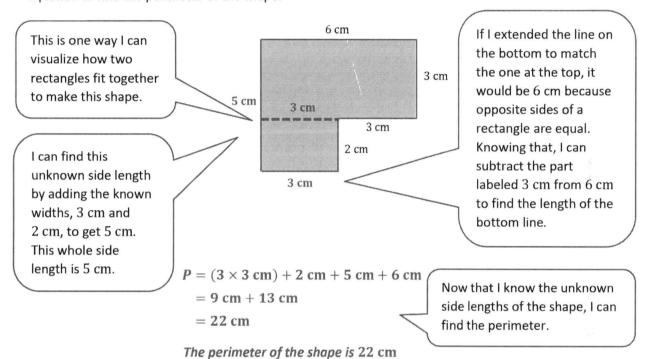

This is one way I can visualize how two rectangles fit together to make this shape.

I can find this unknown side length by adding the known widths, 3 cm and 2 cm, to get 5 cm. This whole side length is 5 cm.

If I extended the line on the bottom to match the one at the top, it would be 6 cm because opposite sides of a rectangle are equal. Knowing that, I can subtract the part labeled 3 cm from 6 cm to find the length of the bottom line.

$$P = (3 \times 3 \text{ cm}) + 2 \text{ cm} + 5 \text{ cm} + 6 \text{ cm}$$
$$= 9 \text{ cm} + 13 \text{ cm}$$
$$= 22 \text{ cm}$$

Now that I know the unknown side lengths of the shape, I can find the perimeter.

The perimeter of the shape is 22 cm

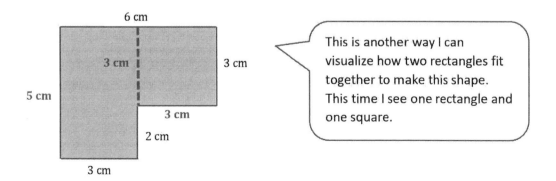

This is another way I can visualize how two rectangles fit together to make this shape. This time I see one rectangle and one square.

Lesson 17: Use all four operations to solve problems involving perimeter and unknown measurements.

25

©2015 Great Minds. eureka-math.org
G3-M7-HWH-1.3.0-10.2015

2. Label the unknown side lengths. Then, find the perimeter of the shaded rectangle.

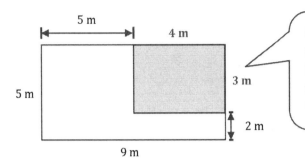

I know the side lengths of the whole rectangle are 9 m and 5 m. In order to find the side lengths of the shaded part, I can subtract the total lengths from the known parts.
9 m − 5 m = 4 m, and 5 m − 2 m = 3 m.

$$P = (2 \times 4 \text{ cm}) + (2 \times 3 \text{ cm})$$
$$= 8 \text{ cm} + 6 \text{ cm}$$
$$= 14 \text{ cm}$$

The perimeter of the shaded rectangle is 14 cm.

Now that I know the side lengths of the shaded part, I can find the perimeter. I know from the question that the shaded part is a rectangle. So it's opposite sides are equal.

©2015 Great Minds. eureka-math.org
G3-M7-HWH-1.3.0-10.2015

G3-M7-Lesson 18

Estimate to draw as many rectangles as you can with an area of 15 square centimeters. Label the side lengths of each rectangle.

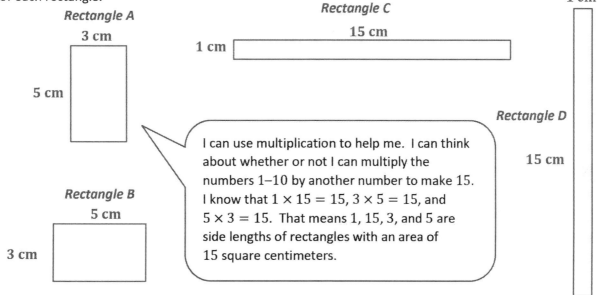

a. Which rectangles above have the greatest perimeter? How do you know just by looking at their shape?

Rectangles C and D have the greatest perimeter. They both have a perimeter of 32 centimeters. I can tell just by looking at their shapes that they have the greatest perimeter because they are longer and skinnier than Rectangles A and B.

I know that long, skinny rectangles have larger perimeters than short, wide rectangles with the same area. Long side lengths add up to greater perimeters than short side lengths.

b. Which rectangles above have the smallest perimeter? How do you know just by looking at their shape?

Rectangles A and B have the smallest perimeter. They both have a perimeter of 16 centimeters. I can tell just by looking at their shapes that they have the smallest perimeter because they are shorter and wider than Rectangles C and D.

I know that short, wide rectangles have smaller perimeters than long, skinny rectangles with the same area. Short side lengths add up to smaller perimeters than long side lengths.

 Lesson 18:   Construct rectangles from a given number of unit squares and determine   27
the perimeters.

©2015 Great Minds. eureka-math.org
G3-M7-HWH-1.3.0-10.2015

G3-M7-Lesson 19

1. Use unit squares to make rectangles for each given number below. Complete the charts to show how many rectangles you can make for each given number of unit squares. You might not use all the spaces in each chart.

Number of unit squares = 12 Number of rectangles I made: __3__	
Width	Length
1	12
2	6
3	4

Number of unit squares = 13 Number of rectangles I made: __1__	
Width	Length
1	13

Number of unit squares = 14 Number of rectangles I made: __2__	
Width	Length
1	14
2	7

13
1 [ ] (row of 13 squares)

4
3

7
2

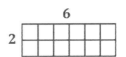
6
2

14
1 [ ] (row of 14 squares)

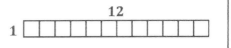
12
1

> I can use multiplication to help me. I can think about whether or not I can multiply the numbers 1–10 by another number to make 12, 13, or 14. Once I figure out factors that equal those numbers when multiplied, I can build rectangles with the factors as the side lengths.

EUREKA MATH

©2015 Great Minds. eureka-math.org
G3-M7-HWH-1.3.0-10.2015

2. Create a line plot with the data you collected in Problem 1.

Number of Rectangles Made with Unit Squares

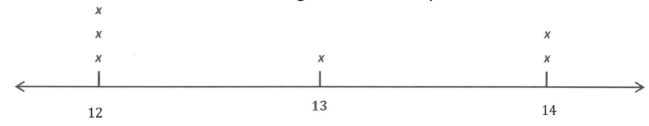

Number of Unit Squares

> I made 3 rectangles with an area of 12 square units, so I'll draw 3 x's above the 12. I can keep going to show how many rectangles I made with 13 and 14 square units.

EUREKA MATH   Lesson 19:   Use a line plot to record the number of rectangles constructed from a given number of unit squares.   29

©2015 Great Minds. eureka-math.org
G3-M7-HWH-1.3.0-10.2015

G3-M7-Lesson 20

1. Rex uses unit square tiles to make rectangles with a perimeter of 12 units. He draws his rectangles as shown below. Can Rex make another rectangle using unit square tiles that has a perimeter of 12 units? Explain your answer.

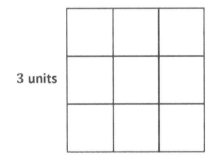

Yes. Rex can also make a square with each side measuring 3 units. Squares are also rectangles. To find the perimeter, I would add $3 + 3 + 3 + 3 = 12$.

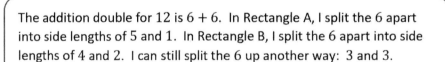

The addition double for 12 is $6 + 6$. In Rectangle A, I split the 6 apart into side lengths of 5 and 1. In Rectangle B, I split the 6 apart into side lengths of 4 and 2. I can still split the 6 up another way: 3 and 3.

Lesson 20:   Construct rectangles with a given perimeter using unit squares and
                        determine their areas.

                        ©2015 Great Minds. eureka-math.org
                        G3-M7-HWH-1.3.0-10.2015

EUREKA MATH

2. Maureen draws a square that has a perimeter of 24 centimeters.

    a. Estimate to draw Maureen's square below. Label the length and width of the square.

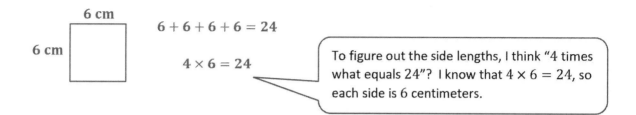

$6 + 6 + 6 + 6 = 24$

$4 \times 6 = 24$

To figure out the side lengths, I think "4 times what equals 24"? I know that $4 \times 6 = 24$, so each side is 6 centimeters.

    b. Find the area of Maureen's square.

$6 \times 6 = 36$

The area of Maureen's square is 36 square centimeters.

I can multiply the side lengths to find the area.

    c. Estimate to draw a different rectangle that has the same perimeter as Maureen's square.

Sample response:

9 cm

3 cm

The addition double for 24 is $12 + 12$. Another pair of numbers that adds up to 12 is 9 and 3.

$9 + 3 + 9 + 3 = 24$

    d. Which shape has a greater area, Maureen's square or your rectangle?

$3 \times 9 = 27$

My rectangle has an area of 27 square centimeters. Maureen's square has a greater area because $36 > 27$.

I can multiply 3×9 to find the area of my rectangle and then compare it to the area of Maureen's square.

EUREKA
MATH™

Lesson 20:   Construct rectangles with a given perimeter using unit squares and
               determine their areas.

31

©2015 Great Minds. eureka-math.org
G3-M7-HWH-1.3.0-10.2015

G3-M7-Lesson 21

1. Max uses unit squares to build rectangles that have a perimeter of 12 units. He creates the chart below to record his findings.

    a. Complete Max's chart. You might not use all the spaces in the chart.

Perimeter = 12 units		
Number of rectangles I made: __3__		
Width	Length	Area
1 unit	5 units	5 square units
2 units	4 units	8 square units
3 units	3 units	9 square units

    > For a perimeter of 12 units, the total of all four side lengths has to be 12 units. I can think about the addition double for 12, which is 6 + 6. That tells me that 6 units should be the sum of the length plus the width. I can find the same information by thinking about 12 ÷ 2.

    > To draw my rectangles, I think about pairs of numbers that equal 6 when I add them. The pairs I use to draw my rectangles are 1 and 5, 2 and 4, and 3 and 3. Then, to find the area of each rectangle, I multiply the side lengths. $1 \times 5 = 5$, $2 \times 4 = 8$, and $3 \times 3 = 9$. Now I can complete the chart.

    b. Explain how you found the widths and lengths in the chart above.

    I know that half of 12 is 6 because 6 + 6 = 12. I thought about different ways to break apart 6. One way to break 6 apart is into 5 and 1. So, one rectangle can have side lengths of 5 units and 1 unit. Another way is 4 and 2. The last way to break apart 6 is 3 and 3. Those numbers became my side lengths.

Lesson 21:   Construct rectangles with a given perimeter using unit squares and determine their areas.

EUREKA
MATH™

2. Grayson and Scarlett both draw rectangles with perimeters of 10 centimeters, but their rectangles have different areas. Explain with words, pictures, and numbers how this is possible.

Grayson's Rectangle

3 cm

2 cm

Scarlett's Rectangle

4 cm

1 cm

First I can think of 2 different ways to make a rectangle with a perimeter of 10 centimeters. Then, I can multiply their side lengths to find the area of each.

Grayson's and Scarlett's rectangles each have a perimeter of 10 centimeters. But the side lengths of their rectangles are different. That's what makes the product of the side lengths different, even though the sum is the same. The area of Grayson's rectangle is 6 square centimeters because $2 \times 3 = 6$. The area of Scarlett's rectangle is 4 square centimeters because $1 \times 4 = 4$.

Lesson 21: Construct rectangles with a given perimeter using unit squares and determine their areas.

©2015 Great Minds. eureka-math.org
G3-M7-HWH-1.3.0-10.2015

33

G3-M7-Lesson 22

1. Jack uses square inch tiles to build a rectangle with a perimeter of 14 inches. Does knowing this help him find the number of rectangles he can build with an area of 14 square inches? Why or why not?

    No, it doesn't. There is no connection between area and perimeter, so knowing how to build a rectangle with a perimeter of 14 inches doesn't help Jack figure out how many rectangles he can build with an area of 14 square inches.

    I've studied area and perimeter a lot in class, and I know that they aren't related. If I want to know how many rectangles I can build with an area of 14 square inches, I can use square tiles or multiplication to figure it out. Thinking about perimeter won't help me.

2. Rachel makes a rectangle with a piece of string. She says the perimeter of her rectangle is 25 centimeters. Explain how it's possible for her rectangle's perimeter to be an odd number.

    Most of the rectangles we've seen had an even perimeter because we usually look at rectangles with whole number side lengths. Rectangles can have odd perimeters if their side lengths are not whole numbers.

    I know that rectangles with whole number side lengths have even perimeters because when you double the sum of whole numbers, you get an even number. Rectangles with fractional side lengths can have odd perimeters if the fractional parts add up to an odd number. For example, if a square has a side length of $\frac{1}{4}$, then the perimeter equals 1 because four copies of $\frac{1}{4}$ makes 1.

Lesson 22:   Use a line plot to record the number of rectangles constructed in Lessons 20 and 21.

©2015 Great Minds. eureka-math.org
G3-M7-HWH-1.3.0-10.2015

EUREKA MATH

G3-M7-Lesson 23

1. Madison uses 4-inch square tiles to make a rectangle, as shown below. What is the perimeter of the rectangle in inches?

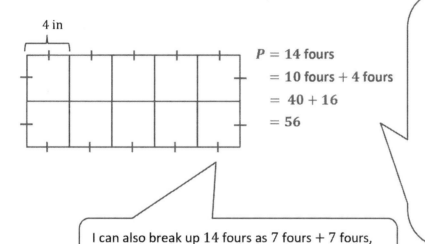

4 in

$P = 14$ fours
$\quad = 10$ fours $+ 4$ fours
$\quad = 40 + 16$
$\quad = 56$

Since Madison uses square tiles, I know that each side length of a tile measures 4 inches. I can then count the total number of side lengths that make up the perimeter of the rectangle, which is 14. Then I can find the perimeter by multiplying 14×4, or in unit form, 14 fours. I can use the break apart and distribute strategy to find the total.

I can also break up 14 fours as 7 fours $+$ 7 fours, but $28 + 28$ is harder mental math than $40 + 16$.

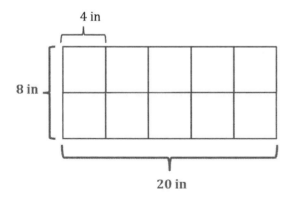

4 in

8 in

20 in

$P = (2 \times 8 \text{ in}) + (2 \times 20 \text{ in})$
$\quad = 16 \text{ in} + 40 \text{ in}$
$\quad = 56 \text{ in}$

Another way to find the perimeter is to find the value of the rectangle's side lengths. I can use repeated addition, skip-counting, or multiplication to find the side lengths. Then, I can double each side length and add to find the perimeter.

The perimeter of the rectangle is 56 inches.

2. David traces 4 regular hexagons to create the shape shown below. The perimeter of 1 hexagon is 18 cm.
    What is the perimeter of David's new shape?

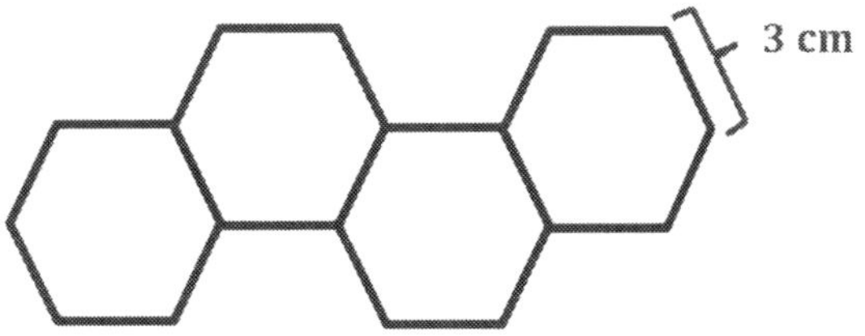

~~ 3 cm

Perimeter of 1 hexagon = 18 cm ÷ 6

                        = 3 cm

> This is a two-step problem. First I need to find the side length of each hexagon. I know David traces regular hexagons, so all of the side lengths are equal. To find the side length, I can divide the perimeter of 1 hexagon, 18 cm, by its 6 sides to get 3 cm.

Perimeter of the shape = 18 × 3 cm

                       = (10 × 3 cm) + (8 × 3 cm)

                       = 30 cm + 24 cm

                       = 54 cm

The perimeter of the shape is 54 cm.

> Next, I can count to find the total number of sides on David's new shape. I can't just multiply 4 × 6 to get the total number of sides because each hexagon shares 1 or 2 sides with another hexagon. I can mark the sides to help me count them. David's new shape has 18 sides. Now I can multiply 18 by 3 cm to get the perimeter of the shape.

Lesson 23:   Solve a variety of word problems with perimeter.

©2015 Great Minds. eureka-math.org
G3-M7-HWH-1.3.0-10.2015

**EUREKA
MATH**

G3-M7-Lesson 24

1. Robin draws a square with a perimeter of 36 inches. What is the width and length of the square?

$36 \div 4 = 9$

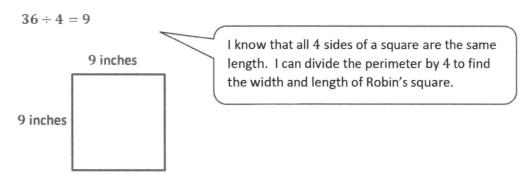

9 inches

9 inches

> I know that all 4 sides of a square are the same length. I can divide the perimeter by 4 to find the width and length of Robin's square.

The width and length of Robin's square are each 9 inches.

2. A rectangle has a perimeter of 16 centimeters.

   a. Estimate to draw as many different rectangles as you can that have a perimeter of 16 centimeters. Label the width and length of each rectangle.

$16 \div 2 = 8$

$1 + 7 = 8$	$w = 1, l = 7$
$2 + 6 = 8$	$w = 2, l = 6$
$3 + 5 = 8$	$w = 3, l = 5$
$4 + 4 = 8$	$w = 4, l = 4$

> I can divide the perimeter by 2 and then find pairs of numbers that have a sum of 8.

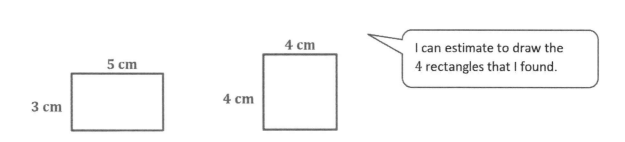

7 cm
1 cm

6 cm
2 cm

5 cm
3 cm

4 cm
4 cm

> I can estimate to draw the 4 rectangles that I found.

EUREKA MATH   Lesson 24:   Use rectangles to draw a robot with specified perimeter measurements, and reason about the different areas that may be produced.   37

©2015 Great Minds. eureka-math.org
G3-M7-HWH-1.3.0-10.2015

b. Explain the strategy you used to find the rectangles.

I divided the perimeter by 2, so 16 ÷ 2 = 8. Then I found pairs of numbers that have a sum of 8. The pairs of numbers that have sums of 8 give me possible whole number side lengths for rectangles with a perimeter of 16 centimeters.

I can divide the perimeter by 2 because the perimeter of a rectangle can be found by adding the width and the length and then multiplying by 2.

Perimeter = 2 × (width + length)

Perimeter ÷ 2 = width + length

Lesson 24:   Use rectangles to draw a robot with specified perimeter measurements, and reason about the different areas that may be produced.

©2015 Great Minds. eureka-math.org
G3-M7-HWH-1.3.0-10.2015

G3-M7-Lesson 25

The house below is made of rectangles and 1 triangle. The side lengths of each rectangle are labeled. Find the perimeter of each rectangle, and record it in the table on the next page.

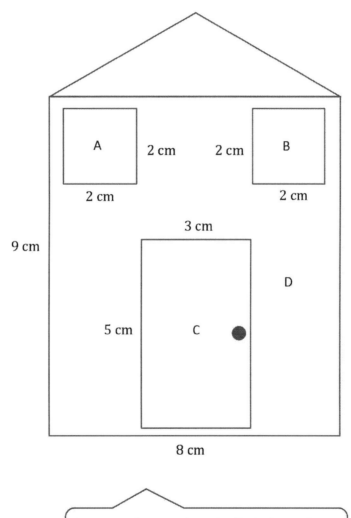

I can see 4 rectangles: the 2 windows, the door, and the outline of the house.

EUREKA MATH   **Lesson 25:**   Use rectangles to draw a robot with specified perimeter measurements, and reason about the different areas that may be produced.   39

©2015 Great Minds. eureka-math.org
G3-M7-HWH-1.3.0-10.2015

Rectangle	Perimeter
A	4×2 cm $= 8$ cm Perimeter $= 8$ cm
B	4×2 cm $= 8$ cm Perimeter $= 8$ cm
C	5 cm $+ 5$ cm $+ 3$ cm $+ 3$ cm $= 16$ cm Perimeter $= 16$ cm
D	8 cm $+ 8$ cm $+ 9$ cm $+ 9$ cm $= 34$ cm Perimeter $= 34$ cm

Rectangles A and B are squares, so I can find the perimeters by multiplying 4×2.

Another strategy I can use to find each perimeter is to add the width and length of the rectangle and then multiply the sum by 2. For Rectangle C, that would look like this:

$P = 2 \times (5 + 3)$

$P = 2 \times 8$

$P = 16$

Lesson 25:   Use rectangles to draw a robot with specified perimeter measurements, and reason about the different areas that may be produced.

EUREKA
MATH

G3-M7-Lesson 26

Each student in Mrs. William's class draws a rectangle with whole number side lengths and a perimeter of 32 centimeters. Then, they find the area of each rectangle and create the table below.

Area in Square Centimeters	Number of Students
15	1
28	2
39	2
48	3
55	4
60	6
63	2
64	2

> I know there can be many different areas for rectangles with the same perimeter.

a. What does this chart tell you about the relationship between area and perimeter?

The chart shows 8 different areas for rectangles with the same perimeter. So, I know that area and perimeter are 2 separate things. There's no connection between them.

b. Did any students in Mrs. William's class draw a square? Explain how you know.

Yes, 2 students drew a square. I know because I found all the possible side lengths of rectangles with a perimeter of 32 cm, and one rectangle has all equal side lengths of 8 cm. A square with side lengths of 8 cm has an area of 64 sq cm. On the chart, it shows that 2 students drew a rectangle with an area of 64 square centimeters.

> Perimeter is double the sum of the width and length of a rectangle. To find the side lengths of a rectangle with a perimeter of 32, I'll start by dividing the perimeter by 2 to get 16. Then, I can find pairs of numbers that add up to 16. Those are the possible side lengths.

c. What are the side lengths of the rectangle that most students in Mrs. William's class made?

I see that most students drew a rectangle with an area of 60 square centimeters. The side lengths of this rectangle are 6 cm and 10 cm.

G3-M7-Lesson 27

Record the perimeters and areas of the rectangles in the chart on the next page.

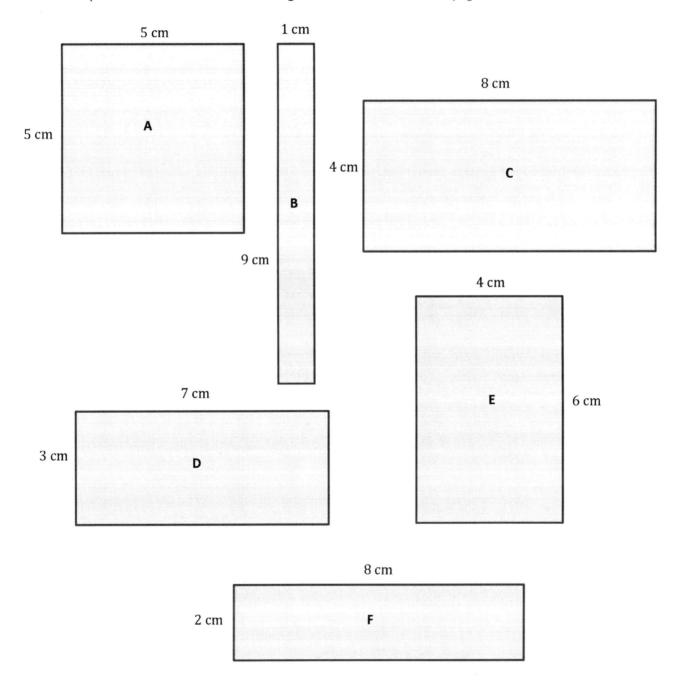

    Lesson 27:   Use rectangles to draw a robot with specified perimeter measurements, and reason about the different areas that may be produced.

EUREKA MATH

I can choose to use mental math to solve for the perimeter and area. I do not need to write out multiplication and addition sentences if I can do it in my head.

1. Find the area and perimeter of each rectangle.

Rectangle	Width and Length	Perimeter	Area
A	__5__ cm by __5__ cm	4×5 cm $= 20$ cm	5 cm $\times$ 5 cm $= 25$ sq cm
B	__9__ cm by __1__ cm	18 cm $+$ 2 cm $= 20$ cm	9 cm $\times$ 1 cm $= 9$ sq cm
C	__4__ cm by __8__ cm	8 cm $+$ 16 cm $= 20$ cm	4 cm $\times$ 8 cm $= 32$ sq cm
D	__3__ cm by __7__ cm	6 cm $+$ 14 cm $= 20$ cm	3 cm $\times$ 7 cm $= 21$ sq cm
E	__6__ cm by __4__ cm	12 cm $+$ 8 cm $= 20$ cm	6 cm $\times$ 4 cm $= 24$ sq cm
F	__2__ cm by __8__ cm	4 cm $+$ 16 cm $= 20$ cm	2 cm $\times$ 8 cm $= 16$ sq cm

2. What do you notice about the perimeters of all the rectangles?

All of the rectangles have different side lengths but the same perimeter of 20 cm.

I can see again how perimeter and area do not have any connection with one another.

3. Which rectangle is a square? How do you know?

Rectangle A is a square. I know because the width and length have the same measurement. Since opposite sides of rectangles are equal, Rectangle A has all equal side lengths and 4 right angles. That means it's a square!

EUREKA MATH™   Lesson 27:   Use rectangles to draw a robot with specified perimeter measurements, and reason about the different areas that may be produced.   43

©2015 Great Minds. eureka-math.org
G3-M7-HWH-1.3.0-10.2015

G3-M7-Lesson 28

A square sheet of construction paper has side lengths of 9 inches.

    a.   Estimate to draw the square sheet of paper, and label the side lengths.

9 in

9 in

> I know that the side lengths of a square are equal.

    b.   What is the area of the square paper?

$$A = 9 \text{ in} \times 9 \text{ in}$$
$$= 81 \text{ sq in}$$

The area of the paper is 81 square inches.

> I found the answer to 9×9 using a tens fact and mental math. I thought about the problem as $9 \times 10 = 90$, and $90 - 9 = 81$.

    c.   What is the perimeter of the square paper?

$$P = 4 \times 9 \text{ in}$$
$$= 36 \text{ in}$$

The perimeter of the square paper is 36 inches.

> I chose to write a multiplication sentence instead of a repeated addition sentence because it is more efficient. I can also think of this problem as $4 \times 10 = 40$, and $40 - 4 = 36$.

Lesson 28:   Solve a variety of word problems involving area and perimeter using all four operations.

EUREKA MATH™

©2015 Great Minds. eureka-math.org
G3-M7-HWH-1.3.0-10.2015

d. Caitlyn connects three of these square papers to make one long banner. What is the perimeter of the new rectangular banner?

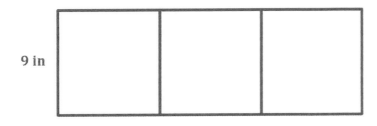

9 in

$P = 8 \times 9 \text{ in}$
$\quad = 72 \text{ in}$

> The side length of each square paper is 9 in. I can count to find that 8 sides of the squares make up the perimeter of the banner.
> $8 \times 9 \text{ in} = 72 \text{ in}$

27 in

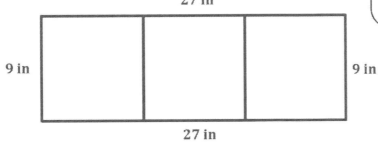

9 in   9 in

27 in

$P = 9 \text{ in} + 9 \text{ in} + 27 \text{ in} + 27 \text{ in}$
$\quad = 72 \text{ in}$

The total perimeter of Caitlyn's banner is 72 inches.

> Another strategy is to first find the side lengths of the rectangle. I know one side of the rectangle is still 9 in, but the other side tripled to 27 in. I can add all the side lengths together, but it's not a very friendly problem. Multiplying, like I did above, is a little easier.

e. What is the total area of Caitlyn's banner?

$A = (3 \times 81 \text{ sq in})$
$\quad = (3 \times 80 \text{ sq in}) + (3 \times 1 \text{ sq in})$
$\quad = 240 \text{ sq in} + 3 \text{ sq in}$
$\quad = 243 \text{ sq in}$

> I can use the break apart and distribute strategy to help me find the answer to this challenging multiplication equation. I can first think of 3×80 in unit form as 3×8 tens = 24 tens, which has a value of 240. Then, I just have to remember to add the product of 3×1.

The total area of Caitlyn's banner is 243 square inches.

Lesson 28:   Solve a variety of word problems involving area and perimeter using all four operations.

©2015 Great Minds. eureka-math.org
G3-M7-HWH-1.3.0-10.2015

G3-M7-Lesson 29

Josh puts two rectangles together to make the L-shaped figure below. He measures some of the side lengths and records them as shown.

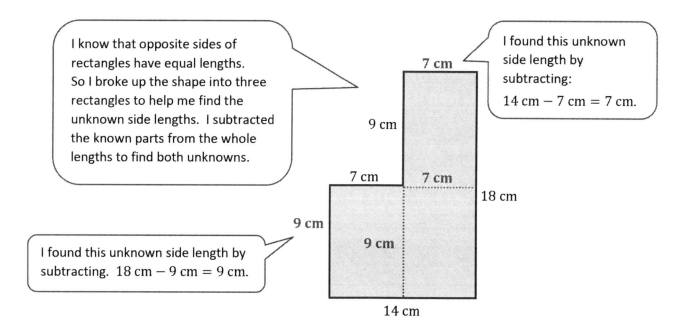

I know that opposite sides of rectangles have equal lengths. So I broke up the shape into three rectangles to help me find the unknown side lengths. I subtracted the known parts from the whole lengths to find both unknowns.

I found this unknown side length by subtracting: $14\ cm - 7\ cm = 7\ cm$.

I found this unknown side length by subtracting. $18\ cm - 9\ cm = 9\ cm$.

a. Find the perimeter of Josh's shape.

$$P = (2 \times 18\ cm) + (2 \times 14\ cm)$$
$$= 36\ cm + 28\ cm$$
$$= 64\ cm$$

The perimeter of Josh's shape is 64 cm.

Lesson 29:   Solve a variety of word problems involving area and perimeter using all four operations.

EUREKA MATH

b. Find the area of Josh's shape.

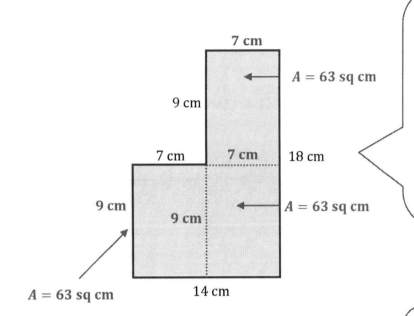

There are many ways to break up this shape. I chose to break it up into 3 rectangles and find the areas of each. I found that each of the three rectangles has an area of 63 sq cm. To find the total area of the shape, I can just add 63 three times or write a multiplication sentence.

$A = 3 \times 63$ sq cm

$= (3 \times 60$ sq cm$) + (3 \times 3$ sq cm$)$

$= 180$ sq cm $+ 9$ sq cm

$= 189$ sq cm

I can use unit form language to help me solve 3×60. It's the same as 3×6 tens. That's equal to 18 tens, which has a value of 180.

The area of Josh's shape is 189 *sq cm.*

G3-M7-Lesson 30

Andrew solves the following problem as shown below.

A basketball court measures 74 feet by 52 feet. Bill dribbles the basketball around the court sidelines 3 times. What is the total number of feet Bill dribbles the ball?

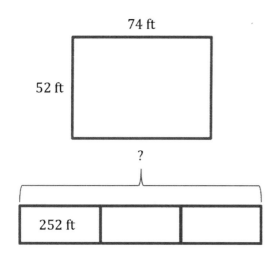

$$P = 52 \text{ ft} + 74 \text{ ft} + 52 \text{ ft} + 74 \text{ ft}$$
$$= 126 \text{ ft} + 126 \text{ ft}$$
$$= 252 \text{ ft}$$

$$252 + 252 + 252$$
$$= 750 + 6$$
$$= 756$$

Bill dribbles the ball 756 feet.

1. What strategies did Andrew use to solve this problem?

   Andrew drew a picture of the basketball court and labeled the side lengths. Then he added to find the perimeter. Finally, he used a tape diagram to find the total of 3 perimeters.

   > Analyzing my classmates' work improves my problem-solving skills because I am able to see different and sometimes more efficient ways of solving a problem.

2. What did Andrew do well?

   Andrew used all the steps in the RDW process. He used mental math for his calculations. He also drew and labeled a tape diagram to show his thinking for his second step.

48   Lesson 30:   Share and critique peer strategies for problem solving.

©2015 Great Minds. eureka-math.org
G3-M7-HWH-1.3.0-10.2015

EUREKA
MATH™

3. What are some suggestions that you would give Andrew to improve his work?

    Some suggestions would be to have Andrew use a letter to represent the unknown in the tape diagram and label all of the units in his addition sentence.

4. What are some strategies you would like to try based on Andrew's work?

    I would like to practice thinking about numbers like $252 + 252 + 252$ as $(250 + 250 + 250) + (2 + 2 + 2)$. That will help me use mental math strategies to add and not have to use the algorithm as much.

> Having classmates analyze my work is helpful because I am able to get ideas on how to improve it.

G3-M7-Lesson 31

1. Use the rectangle below to answer Problem 1 (a)–(d).

a. What is the area of the rectangle in square units?

   The area of the rectangle is 10 square units.

   > I can find the area by multiplying the side lengths.
   > $2 \times 5 = 10$
   > Or, I can count the square units. Either way the answer is the same!

b. What is the area of half of the rectangle in square units?

   $10 \div 2 = 5$

   > I can divide the total area by 2 to find the area of half of the rectangle.

   The area of half of the rectangle is 5 square units.

c. Shade in half of the rectangle above. Be creative with your shading!

   > I can use my answer to part (b) to help me shade in half of the rectangle.

d. Explain how you know you shaded in half of the rectangle.

   I know I shaded in half of the rectangle because I shaded 5 square units and the area of half of the rectangle is 5 square units.

EUREKA
MATH™

©2015 Great Minds. eureka-math.org
G3-M7-HWH-1.3.0-10.2015

2. During art class, Mia draws a shape and then shades one-half of it. Analyze Mia's work. Determine if she was correct or not, and explain your thinking.

Mia's Drawing	Your Analysis
	*Mia did not correctly shaded one-half of her drawing. There is less than one-half of the drawing shaded because of the unshaded heart in the shaded part of the drawing. She needs to shade a same-sized heart in the unshaded part to show one-half shaded.*

I can picture what Mia's drawing might look like if she had shaded it correctly. It might look like this:

3. Shade the grid below to show two different ways of shading half of each shape.

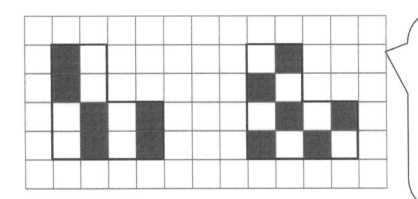

I can find the total area for each shape by counting the square units. Then I can divide that number by 2 to figure out how many square units to shade in order to show one-half. I can shade in 6 square units for each shape.

$12 \div 2 = 6$

©2015 Great Minds. eureka-math.org
G3-M7-HWH-1.3.0-10.2015

G3-M7-Lesson 32

1. Estimate to finish shading the circle below so that it is about one-half shaded.

> I can shade in another half circle that is about the same size as the unshaded half circle.

2. Explain how you know the circle in Problem 1 is about one-half shaded.

I know the circle in Problem 1 is about one-half shaded because I can picture the little shaded half circles flipped over and moved into the shaded part of the circle. Then it would be easy to see that the circle is about one-half shaded because it would look like this:

> I can also picture the large shaded part flipped over onto the unshaded part. Then the circle would look like this:
>
>
>
> Either way, it's easy to see that it's about one-half shaded.

3. Can you say the circle in Problem 1 is exactly one-half shaded? Why or why not?

No, I can't say that the circle in Problem 1 is exactly one-half shaded because there aren't any gridlines, and I had to estimate to shade the little half circle. When I estimate, I know my answer isn't exact.

> I can also tell the circle is not exactly one-half shaded because the directions for Problems 1 and 2 use the word *about*. When I see the word *about* I know the answer is not exact; it's an estimate.

EUREKA MATH

©2015 Great Minds. eureka-math.org
G3-M7-HWH-1.3.0-10.2015

4. Wilson and Laurie shade in circles as shown below.

Wilson's Circle   **Laurie's Circle**

a. Whose circle is about one-half shaded? How do you know?

Laurie's circle is about one-half shaded. I can picture the image in the top part of the circle flipped over and moved to the bottom of the circle. Then the bottom half of Laurie's circle would be all shaded, which means the whole circle would be about one-half shaded.

I see that the shaded amount is about the same as the unshaded amount in Laurie's circle. That means that Laurie's circle is about one-half shaded.

b. Explain how the circle that is not one-half shaded can be changed so that it is one-half shaded.

Wilson's circle has too much shading. He needs to erase a small circle in one of the shaded parts that matches the small shaded circle.

Or, Wilson can erase the small shaded circle. Then his whole circle would be about one-half shaded.

©2015 Great Minds. eureka-math.org
G3-M7-HWH-1.3.0-10.2015

G3-M7-Lesson 33

Teach a family member your favorite fluency game from class. Record information about the game you taught below.

Name of the game:

Partition Shapes

Materials used:

The only materials we needed were personal white boards and markers.

> I can pick any activity from the list my teacher gave me and teach it to someone at home. I know how to play the game by myself, but sometimes you learn something by teaching it to someone else. It helped me think about fractions more when I had to show my sister what we needed to do.

Name of the person you taught to play:

I taught my sister Sonia to play.

Describe what it was like to teach the game. Was it easy? Hard? Why?

I'm used to learning games from my teacher and then playing with friends. Teaching someone else was fun, but it was tricky. Even though I know how to play the game, I realized after we started that I forgot to explain some of the important parts.

Will you play the game together again? Why or why not?

Yes. We liked drawing shapes on our personal white boards. My sister didn't know about fractions, and I got to show her. I liked that. We'll try different games sometimes too.

Was the game as fun to play at home as in class? Why or why not?

It was really fun to play at home because I also got to teach it to my sister.